101 SIMPLE EXPERIMENTS
WITH INSECTS

101
Simple Éxperiments
With Insects

H. KALMUS

M.D. (Prague), D.Sc. (Prague)
University College, London

DOUBLEDAY & COMPANY, INC.
GARDEN CITY, NEW YORK

PUBLISHER'S NOTE

Doubleday & Company, Inc., wishes to acknowl-
edge its indebtedness to Rebecca Hutto Witherspoon and James Donald Witherspoon, of the
Department of Biological Sciences at Purdue
University, for their aid in adapting those few
sections of the book where such adaptation was
deemed necessary to make the text fully applicable
to North American readers.

Preface

There are probably many thousands, if not millions, of amateur entomologists in the world, not counting every child who is interested in beetles or butterflies; modern life is not likely to result in any decrease in their numbers but rather, by its very monotony, will tend to increase them. The beetle-collecting enthusiast, however, is usually considered rather ridiculous by his fellow citizens. I think that one reason for this is that he has not kept abreast with modern developments in his hobby. He still clings to the old techniques of collecting, preserving, and labeling (as well as he can), in what is really a hopeless competition with the big museums.

Now, it will not be denied that the collecting of specimens and the taking of notes on observations is an occupation that is not only worth while but even necessary for the expansion of our knowledge of the natural sciences. But entomology has not escaped the fate of all developing sciences, having become more and more experimental and more and more mathematical. Of these two aspects, the experimental will make the greater appeal to the majority of "amateurs"—to school children and to their teachers. Consequently, it is hoped that this small collection of simple experiments may meet a demand from amateurs of all types. It is not intended to be a scientific introduction to the modern and rapidly growing subject of insect physiology, or to its applications in agriculture, medicine, and other applied sciences. Such an introduction has been admirably provided by Wigglesworth in his *Introduction to Insect Physiology,* and in such books as von Budden-brock's *Grundriss der vergleichenden Physiologie.*

Insect physiology began, as all biological sciences have begun, in the anecdotal vein, and so it has remained until very recently. Some people, such as some of our older bee-keepers, will probably never wish to leave this stage. Later, the subject has suffered from analogies being drawn between insect and human physiology. It is perhaps worth while to point out here one of the fundamental differences, which is often overlooked, between the physiology of an insect and that of a man; namely, the different relationships between circulation and respiration in the two cases. Up to a point, the classical authors were aware of the difference. Aristotle characterized the vertebrates by their possession of red blood, while Pliny suggested that inside an insect there is nothing but air. In modern terms the difference can be described as follows: the oxygen of the atmosphere reaches the tissues of an insect almost directly by way of the tracheal system; whereas in the vertebrate it is first dissolved in the blood, where it is absorbed by the hemoglobin of the red corpuscles, and is then released in the capillaries of the tissues—such as the brain, the muscles, and the glands.

The death of an individual is usually taken to be synchronous with the cessation of the brain's functioning. When a man's heart stops beating, his brain will not get enough oxygen, and in a few seconds it will stop working. No revival is possible without restoration of the circulation —which does not usually occur once the brain has become inactive. In the case of an insect, however, the circulation is much less important so far as the movements of gases are concerned; so that an insect may be kept in an oxygen-free atmosphere for many hours, sometimes even for days, and can still be revived merely by bringing it back into air.

Other more obvious differences between most insects and man are that the former have no means of temperature regulation; they possess an external instead of an internal skeleton; they are of a very much smaller size, with all the implications that follow upon this; and there is less plasticity in their nervous reactions, usually called instincts. All these aspects have, up to a point, been considered in collecting these experiments.

Only such experiments are described as have been performed, or at least witnessed, by the author, whether in the actual form described or in some other form. (The figures in parentheses after the title of each experiment refer to the original description, as listed in the bibliography at the end of the book.) Some are of extreme simplicity and can be performed with no apparatus at all, while others are more suitable for use as class demonstrations. Even the most elaborate apparatus used can be produced by a mechanically minded schoolboy. Thus it is hoped that not many failures will occur when the experiments are actually tried. The author would, however, be grateful for full reports of such failures, since both amateur and professional scientists may sometimes learn more from the failure of an experiment than from its success.

Without the help of Miss L. M. Crump this book could not have been produced, and the author wishes therefore to thank her sincerely for her co-operation. Suggestions made by Mr. Eric Lucas and Mr. Alan Dale, both of whom kindly read the MS. and proofs, have been gratefully incorporated.

H. Kalmus

SECOND IMPRESSION

In the Second Impression of this book a number of minor corrections have been made, following suggestions from reviewers and readers. However, the progress of experimental entomology during the last decade, though great, has not brought forward many new *simple* experiments; and thus the main features of the book remain unaltered.

H.K.

Galton Laboratory,
University College, London
March 1958

Contents

On Insects in General

It is difficult to assess the number of insect species that are actually known. Estimates have been given varying between one and a half million and half a million. But, in any case, there is little doubt that there are more species of insects alive on the earth than there are species of all the other groups of animals put together. In all this vast diversity of forms, however, there is one fundamental type of bodily structure which all insects have in common and which very rarely leaves any room for doubt as to whether a specimen (at any rate, an adult specimen) is an insect or not. Insects belong to the group Arthropoda and are characterized, as a rule, by possessing six walking legs on the middle part of the body; to this they owe their Latin name Hexapoda. The middle part, or thorax, is separated from the head in front, and from the abdomen behind, by deep constrictions; and it is because of these constrictions that the Hexapodae are also called Insecta or Entoma (meaning "cut in"). Among the arthropods, which include the insects, the crustaceans, and the spiders, the insects are the only forms which may carry one or two pairs of wings on the thorax (but there are also, of course, insects without wings). The largest insects are found among the moths and beetles—some of these being larger than the smallest vertebrates, such as some of the hummingbirds. Other beetles or parasitic wasps may be very small—even smaller than some of the Protozoa, e.g., the largest Infusoria. The maximum size of an insect is probably limited by the efficiency of the tracheal system; this depends mainly on the speed of diffusion of the respiratory gases, which in some cases is helped to a slight extent by respiratory movements (Experiment 15). The lower limit of size is probably determined by the difficulty of preventing too great a loss of moisture from the body when it is exposed to a dry environment (Experiment 1).

Insects, like all arthropods, have an outside skeleton. This is a more or less hard cuticle, one of whose constituents is chitin. It combines the functions of both the skeleton and the skin, which in vertebrates are usually separate. Many of the muscles in insects, e.g., the wing muscles in the thorax, are inserted on internal processes of the cuticle. The head of an adult insect carries one pair of antennae, together with the mouth parts (mandibles, maxillae, and labium). These vary very much according to the food of the species and are described as either "biting" or "sucking." In addition, the head generally carries a pair of compound eyes and three ocelli. The thorax bears the three pairs of legs, and the wings when these are present. The abdomen has from six to twelve segments, which, in the adult, do not carry any walking legs but may have other appendages, such as the forceps in the earwig. The external structure of an insect is shown in Fig. 1.

The intestinal tract consists of a long gut with various regions, such as the crop and the stomach, and accessory organs, such as the salivary glands. It also contains structures which are peculiar to insects—the six Malpighian tubes (called after the famous Italian naturalist Malpighi). These join the gut near its hindmost end and are organs of excretion analogous to the vertebrate kidney.

The basic pattern of the central nervous system is the

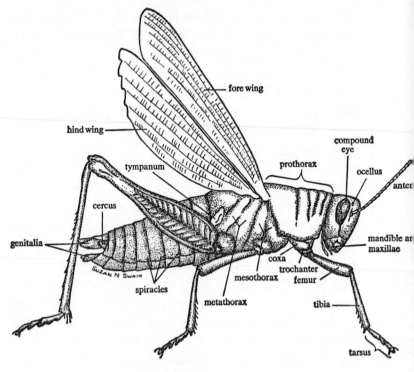

Fig. 1. The external structure of an insect.

(Drawing by SuZan Noguchi Swain, from *Living Insects of the World*, by Alexander B. and Elsie B. Klots. Reprinted by permission of Doubleday & Company, Inc., and Chanticleer Press, Inc., New York.)

same in all insects. There is a brain composed of masses of nerve cells collected around the forepart of the gut, and a double ventral nerve cord with segmental ganglia. The circulatory system, which is very different from that of the vertebrates, consists of a heart and blood vessels; but there are no capillaries. The body fluid (blood) surrounds the heart and enters it by lateral openings. This fluid is pumped into the various regions of the body and returns again to the main body cavity. The respiratory or tracheal system consists of hollow invaginated tubes, which are reinforced by spirals of chitin. The openings of the main tracheae to the outside world are the spiracles. The inside ends of the tracheae are branched, and the finer ramifications form a network providing a supply of air for most of the organs and tissues. Hence they are comparable to the vertebrate blood capillaries.

In most species of insects there are males and females. In the male there are two testes, each consisting of a few lobules, which release the sperms through a duct into which various glands also discharge their secretions. The females usually have two groups of ovaries, which are connected to oviducts that end in a common vagina. Into this open the glands which add the shell to the eggs. There are also various receptacles joined to the oviducts which receive the sperms from the males. The relative positions of the various organs are shown in Fig. 2.

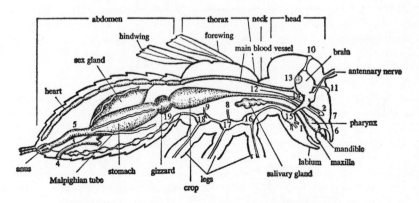

Fig. 2. Diagram of section through the body of an insect. 1. salivary duct; 2. frontal ganglion; 3. sex duct; 4. opening of sex organs; 5. hind intestine; 6. labrum; 7. labial nerve; 8, 9. alary nerves; 10. median ocellus; 11. lateral ocellus; 12. oesophagus; 13. optic lobe; 14. oesophageal ganglion; 15. suboesophageal ganglion; 16, 17, 18. thoracic ganglia; 19. first abdominal ganglion.

Primitive insects probably had a gradual development without a pronounced pupal stage; but in forms where the larvae and the adults lead very different lives in widely differing habitats, a pupal stage is necessary, during which the reorganization of the insect is effected. An example is the mosquito, where the larva is aquatic and the adult lives in the air. The physiology also of maggots and caterpillars is very different from that of flies and butterflies.

The experiments in this book are roughly grouped according to the organs and systems with which they are concerned, and to the functions of these organs. It is difficult, however, to classify physiological experiments in any hard and fast way, as any one experiment may have a bearing on many questions.

CHAPTER I

Metabolism

EXPERIMENT 1. Drying Up of Soil Collembola
(80)

Animals and apparatus: Collembola from soil; petri dishes; filter paper.

Many insects are in perpetual danger of drying up (Experiment 28), and various devices are employed to avoid this fate. Insects that live in dry air and feed on dry food have various physical and chemical means of protecting themselves from excessive loss of moisture. But those insects that normally live in a moist or vapor-saturated environment dry up at once when they are exposed to air which is deficient in moisture. A good example of this is found in some of the soil insects, and in particular in the small wingless Collembola, or springtails. In a handful of soil from a plowed field one can usually find a number of these small animals, ranging in color from white to brown or dark blue, according to the species. If some of them are put on filter paper soaked with water in a petri dish, they will live there under a cover as long as there is any water left—sometimes for more than a day. If, on the other hand, they are put into a dry petri dish they will die within a few minutes.

NOTE. The numbers in parentheses following the experimental titles refer to the relevant sources in the Bibliography (pp. 179–82).

It is possible that some of the Collembola take up water by means of a funnel-shaped organ on the under surface of the body; and probably this is what happens in the soil, since any normal soil contains enough capillary water to saturate the air which is present in the air spaces.

EXPERIMENT 2. Production of Water by Insects

Animals and apparatus: Bees or blowflies; pint bottle and cork; blue litmus paper.

As most body constituents (such as proteins, fats, and carbohydrates) contain hydrogen in addition to carbon, it follows that water as well as carbon dioxide will always be produced by oxidation; and that some water will be lost through the spiracles whenever these are opened to allow of the diffusion of oxygen and carbon dioxide. The mechanisms controlling the width of the opening of the spiracles, which are sometimes very elaborate, are in fact probably devices to cut down the loss of water from the tracheal system as far as is compatible with the demand for oxygen at any given time. If this is true, one would expect there to be not only an increased production of carbon dioxide in periods of great muscular activity but also an increased loss of water.

That this occurs can be shown in an experiment using either bees or blowflies. A few of the insects are put into a pint bottle, and a strip of dry blue litmus paper is held between the cork and the neck of the bottle, so that it projects into the bottle and above the cork. If the insects are fluttering about, the color of the paper in the bottle will change to pink in a few seconds; but if they are sitting quietly on the walls, it will take many minutes for the color change to occur. In damp conditions, the paper protruding from the bottle will also change color gradually.

Blue litmus paper is prepared by soaking filter paper in a 5 per cent solution of cobalt chloride and drying it. If it is carefully dried after a test, it can be used again.

EXPERIMENT 3. Light Production by Fireflies (8, 49)

Animals and apparatus: Firefly; bottle; watch with second hand; warm water; iced water.

In North America, when luminescent insects are mentioned we immediately think of fireflies. The rhythmic twinkling of lights from their abdomens make many summer evenings more pleasant. Biologists postulate that the luminescence enables male and female adults to find each other for mating purposes. This may be true, but it leaves unexplained the glimmer of certain firefly larvae, the "glowworms."

The cold light called bioluminescence originates in a heatless chemical reaction. In this reaction oxygen combines with a substance called luciferin in the presence of the enzyme luciferase. When the light turns off, the chemicals are restored to their original condition in preparation for the next flash. Fireflies glow every few seconds; the rate and duration vary with the species and temperature.

Catch a firefly and place it in a small bottle. Count the frequency of flashes and note also their relative brightness and duration. Now partly submerge the bottle in ice-cold water. Again count the flashes. As cold penetrates the firefly's body, its activity decreases and so also does the rate and brilliance of its light. Conditions are no longer optimal for the oxidation of luciferin. Now remove the bottle from cold water and place it in warm. Watch how the flashes speed up, eventually reaching a rate greater than normal.

EXPERIMENT 4. The Mineral Requirements of
Drosophila (69, 74)

Animals and apparatus: Drosophila flies; twenty-four
flat-bottomed specimen tubes 1 inch by 5 inches; etherizer; food medium; filter paper; cotton wool.

Drosophila melanogaster (or fruit fly), which is used in
many of the experiments described in this book, is usually
bred on a rather complex medium, in the way that is described on page 170. However, it was shown in 1915 that it
can be bred on a medium containing potassium phosphate
and magnesium sulphate as the only salts. Actually the
larvae of *Drosophila* feed on the yeasts or other micro-
organisms that grow on the food medium; and therefore
only the requirements of the double system, *Drosophila*
and yeast, can be investigated in a simple way. The adult
flies can readily live on mixtures of water and sugar, although they do not produce eggs under these conditions
(Experiment 8). The deposition of eggs and the development of the offspring can be made the subject of experi-
mentation by using a sucrose solution as a basis and by
adding to it various other compounds. If the right concentrations and combinations are used in such an experiment,
much can be learned about the metabolism of this fly and
about nutritional experiments in general.

For this experiment twenty-four specimen tubes are
needed, each being 1 inch in diameter and 5 inches long;
these are labeled from 1 to 24, and every tube is filled
with 10 cc. of a solution containing: 10.0 gms. agar, 2.5
gms. tartaric acid, and 40.0 gms. sugar in 500 cc. of water.
(If a chemical balance is not available, the quantities
should be: ½ oz. agar, ⅛ oz. tartaric acid, and 2 ozs.
sugar in one pint of water.) All the ingredients should be

boiled until the agar is completely melted, and the solution should be put into the tubes while it is still as hot as possible. Three other solutions are also needed:

(a) 1.5 gms. potassium acid phosphate in 50 cc. of water.

(b) 2.0 gms. ammonium sulphate in 50 cc. of water.

(c) 0.5 gms. magnesium sulphate in 50 cc. of water.

The following table shows the way in which these solutions are used and the number of drops of each that must be added to the different tubes:

| | | Solutions | |
Tubes	(a)	(b)	(c)
1–3	0	0	0
4–6	6	0	0
7–9	6	8	0
10–12	6	0	2
13–15	6	8	2
16–18	0	8	0
19–21	0	8	2
22–24	0	0	2

It will be seen that all the possible combinations of the three salts are present in triplicate. All the solutions should be used hot, and a piece of filter paper an inch square should be put into each tube to keep the liquid from moving about too freely. Finally, the tubes are stoppered with cotton-wool plugs and left to cool.

About one hundred *Drosophila* flies are lightly etherized (see page 168), and two females and one male (see Fig. 39) are transferred with a paintbrush onto the filter paper in each tube (taking care that the insects do not get stuck). The flies always carry some yeast cells on their bodies, and there are usually enough of these present to inoculate the media; often bacterial colonies of various colors develop, too, but for the purposes of this experiment this does not make a great difference. On the other hand, molds may invalidate the results and, where molds have

grown, erratic results will often be found. After a short
interval all the tubes are inspected to make sure that no
flies have been drowned; if any have been, they are replaced by living insects. All the tubes are then collected
in a box together and put in a warm place, the temperature
of which should be between 20°C. and 28°C.

After three days larvae can be observed in some of the
tubes, and after seven days the first pupae will appear;
after ten to fifteen days, depending on the temperature,
the first young flies will emerge. Their number should be
counted every day and entered on a list. After about a
month the experiment is usually finished, and then the results can be surveyed. First the numbers are examined,
and an average of each set of three replicates is taken,
leaving out any result where an accident has obviously
occurred. The averages may be plotted against the composition of the media; and if everything has worked normally, there should be no yield in tubes 1–3 and most flies
in tubes 13–15. The other tubes can be grouped into those
in which each of the three salts is either absent or present,
and thus the effect of the various constituents on productivity can be assessed.

Experimental designs similar to the one described here
can be used to solve nutritional problems of many kinds,
in a relatively quick and efficient way.

EXPERIMENT 5. Culture of *Drosophila* on Milk
(27)

Animals and apparatus: See Experiment 4.

The normal diet of *Drosophila* larvae is yeast. But they
can feed equally well, or even better, on other micro-
organisms, e.g., milk bacteria. This can easily be demonstrated by an experiment similiar to Experiment 4. For
this purpose, only twelve specimen tubes are needed, of

which three contain 10 cc. of 8 per cent sugar solution, three contain 8 cc. of sugar solution and 2 cc. of skim milk, the next three have 5 cc. of sugar solution and 5 cc. of skim milk, and the last three 10 cc. of skim milk alone. A square inch of filter paper is put into the liquid in each tube, and all tubes are then kept for a day in a warm room, so that the milk goes sour. About fifty flies are etherized; two females and one male are transferred into each tube with the precautions described above; and the yields are recorded in the same way as in Experiment 4.

EXPERIMENT 6. Immobilization by Chilling and Heating

Animals and apparatus: Fly, bee, or any small flying insect; test tube; cotton wool; block of ice or ice cream; refrigerator or vacuum flask; tumbler; hot water; thermometer registering to 60°C.

The proper functioning of the body in an insect is not so dependent on a relatively constant temperature as it is in the mammals and birds; nevertheless, most insect activities can normally be carried out only within a certain temperature range. The easiest way of determining this range is to observe the neuromuscular activity (body movements) of an insect at various temperatures. A housefly, or a bee, or any other flying insect, is put into a test tube which is closed with a plug of cotton wool. If the tube is then rested on an ice block such as is made in a refrigerator, or on a block of ice cream, the movements of the insect soon become sluggish; it will fall down, and after a few unco-ordinated movements of the legs it will stop moving altogether. When the test tube is removed from the ice, or the insect is shaken out onto a piece of paper, after a few seconds the insect will start moving again; it will turn over and walk, or possibly fly, away. A speedy recovery can also be observed after several hours' chilling in a refrigerator or ice-filled vacuum flask.

Immobilization can also be seen to occur at high temperatures, if the test tube containing the insect is submerged in a tumbler of water heated to $45°-50°$C. After a few seconds of agitation most small insects will fall down and cease moving; if they are left at this temperature for more than a few seconds, they either will not recover at all or will recover incompletely after a very long time. But even if they are removed quickly, their recovery will be much slower than it is after cooling.

In applied biology, use is made of both high and low temperatures for fighting insects; but whereas sufficiently high temperatures will quickly kill a pest or a parasite, low temperatures will as a rule only slow down or temporarily stop their development.

EXPERIMENT 7. Activation of Insects by Human Breath (58)

Animals and apparatus: Young stick insects, etc.; metal tube; glass tube; cotton wool; dehydrated calcium chloride; rubber tubing; wash bottle with 25 per cent caustic potash solution.

Motionless stick insects or ants, butterflies which are still chilly in the morning, or sleeping mosquitoes on a wall, will all become active if they are breathed upon.

The air leaving the human mouth or nose is usually at a temperature of about $37°$C., is vapor-saturated, contains between 3 and 4 per cent of carbon dioxide and a somewhat reduced percentage of oxygen, and in addition is in motion. Several of these factors are concerned in the activation of many insects.

It is easy to separate the various factors in a series of simple experiments. The temperature can be reduced by breathing through a cold metal tube; although water will condense on the inner walls of the tube, so that the air coming out of it will contain absolutely less water vapor, yet it will still be moisture-saturated at the lower temperature. Moisture can be completely removed from the breath by blowing through a tube containing grains of dehydrated calcium chloride; while by washing the air in a solution of warm potassium hydroxide in a wash bottle, the carbon dioxide can be removed without lowering the temperature. Finally, it is possible to reduce the air flow by blowing through a glass tube blocked with cotton wool; if this tube is held in a warm hand and the insects themselves are enclosed between cotton-wool stoppers, the quality of the exhaled air will not be very much changed. Using these methods, it will be found that in many species heat, moisture, and CO_2, either singly or combined, will increase the motor activity to varying degrees. The direction of the animal's movement usually bears no relation to the direction of the air current, but sometimes it may; such reactions are described in Experiments 46 and 47.

EXPERIMENT 8. Survival of Flies on Mixtures of Sugar and Water (38, 67)

Animals and apparatus: Drosophila flies one to two days old; test tubes; sugar; cotton wool.

Many adult insects can live on comparatively simple diets, while some, e.g., the May fly, do not feed at all as adults. In some other species, egg laying is dependent on special kinds of protein-rich food, this being the case with the bedbug and the mosquito, where the males can live on nectar alone. It has been found that houseflies and blowflies can actually live many times longer on a sugar diet than when they are fed on meat—though meat is usually regarded as being a more natural food, at least in the case of blowflies. But on the simpler diet neither insect lays eggs. The same thing applies in the case of *Drosophila*.

Drosophila can be used for a demonstration of the dependence of the length of life on moisture and carbohydrates. For this purpose ten test tubes may be used, containing various mixtures of sugar and water. In the first tube the bottom is covered with dry sugar; in the second, eight saltspoonfuls of sugar are moistened with one of water; in the third, seven of sugar with two of water; and so on until pure water is reached in the tenth tube. The tubes are then numbered, and some filter paper or cotton wool is put into each to provide a foothold for the flies and to prevent them from getting soiled by the liquid. Ten *Drosophila* flies, from one to two days old (page 170), are then put into each tube, and all the tubes are stoppered with cotton wool and put away in a temperate room (about 20°C.). On the following days notes are made as to how many flies are dead in each tube; and when all the flies are dead, graphs can be drawn plotting the times when five flies had died at each sugar concentration, against the percentage of sugar present; or the time of death of the last fly in each tube can be plotted. When this is done a graph like the one shown in Fig. 3 will be obtained, indicating that where there was an optimum mixture of sugar and water the flies lived the longest. The optimum will be found to occur in the neighborhood of 20 per cent of sugar; under these conditions there are enough calories to maintain life, and also enough water to compensate for water loss; but no eggs are laid. The addition of very little yeast or milk to a 15 per cent sugar solution contained in an additional tube will often result in a rich culture of *Drosophila*.

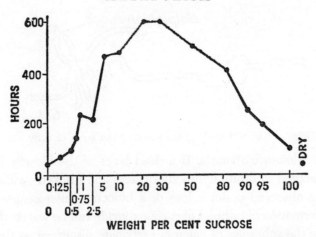

Fig. 3. Time of survival (in hours) of *Drosophila* flies
fed on mixtures containing various percentages of sugar
in water.

Some other sugars—such as glucose, fructose, maltose,
and mannose—will also sustain the flies for a long time;
while others—xylose and arabinose, for instance—will not.
The technique described can also be used to investigate
other problems, such as the relation of temperature to
length of survival.

EXPERIMENT 9. Calcium Carbonate in the
Malpighian Tubes of Diptera (30)

Animals and apparatus: Larvae of *Drosophila* and blowflies; strong lens or binocular microscope; dilute hydrochloric acid; glass slide; needles; dilute potassium hydroxide if
desired.

In the larvae of *Drosophila* the two longest Malpighian
tubes (Fig. 4) are filled with a white shining suspension
consisting of spherical granules of calcium carbonate. In
many other Diptera, too, the Malpighian tubes are loaded

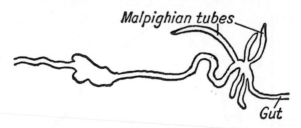

Fig. 4. Gut and Malpighian tubes of the larva of a fly.

with calcium carbonate. If a dead larva of the blowfly is submerged in dilute hydrochloric acid and pricked—while being observed under a lens or a binocular microscope—the formation of bubbles of carbon dioxide can be watched, while the spherules of calcium carbonate disappear as the calcium chloride which is formed goes into solution. It can be proved that this gas is carbon dioxide by adding a drop of diluted potassium hydroxide solution; potassium carbonate will be formed, and the bubbles will disappear. An alternative method is to tear the larva in two with needles and let it dry on a slide with the Malpighian tubes spread out; if dilute hydrochloric acid is then poured onto the slide, the formation of bubbles of gas from the powder can be seen.

EXPERIMENT 10. Recovery from Cyanide Poisoning (5, 68)

N.B. This experiment should be performed only with the aid of an instructor or otherwise qualified person.

Animals and apparatus: Houseflies, blowflies, fruit flies; coal gas; killing bottle; siphon.

Hydrocyanic acid is very poisonous to most animals and plants; its main action is to block the oxidizing enzymes, so that respiration becomes impossible. In man, or in any other vertebrate, the nerve centers regulating the respiratory movements of the thorax and abdomen rapidly become paralyzed when hydrocyanic acid gas is breathed in; and once this stage is reached the poison cannot be removed from the central nervous system, as respiration has stopped. In addition, the poison is carried by the blood stream and the action of the heart is also soon inhibited. In insects, respiratory movements are not so important as they are in the vertebrates, and in many small insects they may even be completely lacking. The gases in the air are not transported by the blood as they are in most other animals, but have direct access to the tissues by means of the tracheae. Consequently, poisoning by gases, which is usually irreversible in vertebrates, is often reversible in insects. This can easily be demonstrated by means of a cyanide killing bottle such as is used by entomologists.

If several flies—houseflies, blowflies, or fruit flies—of the same age are put into the cyanide bottle, they are immobilized within a few seconds or minutes—the exact time depending on the concentration of hydrocyanic acid gas in the bottle. If single insects are then removed from the bottle one at a time, they will recover after intervals, which increase in length with the increase in the time of exposure to the poison, until a stage of intoxication is reached at which recovery is no longer possible. If enough insects are used, a curve can be obtained by plotting the time of exposure to the cyanide in the bottle against the time of recovery.

The recovery time of a cyanide-poisoned insect can be greatly shortened by exposing it to an atmosphere of carbon dioxide or coal gas, or of various other gases (not oxygen or nitrogen). Carbon dioxide not only makes the spiracles gape, thus increasing the diffusion of gases in and out of the tracheal system and tissues, but it also may oust the cyanide from its labile attachment to the respiratory enzymes—a process which is comparable to the liberation of hydrocyanic acid from the potassium cyanide in a killing bottle by the carbon dioxide in the atmosphere.

If other insects are used for this experiment, it will be found that there is great variation in the resistance of the different genera; the burnet moth is particularly resistant. Considerable differences in resistance have also been observed among the species, and even between individuals, of many pests when cyanide is being used as a means of control, and it seems that cyanide resistance can thus be selective.

EXPERIMENT 11. Killing a Fly with Cigarette Smoke

Animals and apparatus: Housefly; glass tube; two corks or rubber stoppers; cigarette.

It is generally known that nicotine is a very good insecticide, and this can be demonstrated in a simple way. A housefly is enclosed in a glass tube about 12 inches long and ½ inch in diameter which can be closed with a cork at each end. The fly is confined in the tube between loosely packed bits of cotton wool. Smoke from a cigarette is blown into the open tube, preferably smoke which has not been inhaled, and when it comes out densely at the far end, both ends are corked. After about two minutes the fly will lose its ability to stand and may be seen lying on its back giving short, rhythmical jerks with its legs; after another minute or so it will be quite motionless; and when it is shaken out of the tube it will remain motionless for about five minutes. After this it will gradually show signs of recovery, stand up, clean itself, and even fly away. Longer exposure to smoke, which, however, must be supplemented every minute or so, will ultimately kill the fly. The toxic action of the nicotine is probably enhanced by the 3–4 per cent of carbon dioxide in the expiratory air (Experiment 7), which keeps the spiracles open. Nevertheless, if the smoke, instead of being blown into the tube, is drawn through it directly by inserting a cigarette at one end and sucking the air out at the other, a toxic action will still be observed.

CHAPTER II

Digestion

EXPERIMENT 12. The Feeding of Female Mosquitoes before Egg Laying

Animals and apparatus: Mosquitoes; two large glass jars; muslin; rubber band.

Many mosquitoes (as well as a variety of other insects) can lay eggs only after a meal of blood. They usually start egg laying one or two days after this event, and feeding as well as egg laying can be observed in some species in the following way. Females of the genus *Culex* can easily be collected in a stable at most times of the year, and if they are hungry they may be induced to feed on one's arm. In countries where endemic malaria and yellow fever occur, care must be taken not to confuse *Culex* species with those of *Anopheles* and *Aëdes*. A large glass jar into which the arm can be put is provided with a muslin cap; this cap should have a hole in it through which the mosquitoes and the arm can be inserted and the hole can be closed with a rubber band. The mosquitoes may be caught in a tumbler with a piece of card slipped over the top, and transferred to the jar. When there are about a dozen assembled, the bare arm, previously washed in hot water so that the skin is soft and warm, is put into the jar through the hole in the muslin cap, and the mosquitoes are watched. After feeding for about a minute they become quite fat and reddish. To induce them to lay eggs, another large glass jar closed with muslin is used, in which some dead leaves or a little hay is submerged in about an inch of water with a few twigs projecting above the surface. The blood-filled mosquitoes are shaken into it, care being taken to see that they do not get wet. This jar is then put away in a fairly warm place. After two or three days eggs will be found on the surface of the water, either singly in *Anopheles* or in little clusters in *Culex,* and after a further two days the small larvae will emerge; these will grow in the infusion and will show the reactions described in Experiment 68.

Some people react more violently to mosquito bites than others, especially if they have been bitten before. It is believed that the local swelling of the skin is due to a reaction with the mosquito's saliva, or possibly to the presence of some minute organisms living in the saliva. Washing the arm with soap after it has been bitten will usually help to relieve the swelling.

EXPERIMENT 13. Digestion of a Meal of Blood in the Mosquito

Animals and apparatus: Mosquitoes; apparatus as in Experiment 12; killing bottle (page 169); fine needles; lens or binocular microscope.

Mosquitoes, bugs, fleas, lice, and other blood-sucking insects fill their stomachs full enough at a meal for the red color of the blood to be seen in the swollen abdomen. After a day or so the swelling gradually disappears and the red coloration, which is due to the hemoglobin, gradually changes into the brown of hematin. Hematin does not contain the protein of the blood corpuscles, i.e., the globin, which is specific for the species from which the blood has been taken; this fraction is digested in the stomach of the blood-sucking insect and is therefore not present any longer once the red color of the stomach contents has changed into brown. A practical consequence of this is that the stomach contents of a mosquito can be used for only twenty-four hours after a meal for a determination by serological tests of the host from which the blood came; this is important in investigating the habits of malaria mosquitoes, which may feed on men or cattle. In mosquitoes fed as described in Experiment 12, several stages in the breakdown of hemoglobin can be observed by killing individuals one, two, and three days after the blood meal and dissecting them. An account of a more complex mode of the disintegration of a blood meal, leading to the deposition of green and blue pigments (porphyrins) in various tissues of a tropical bug, *Rhodnius,* can be found in a paper by Wigglesworth (99). These pigments are identical with those coloring bruises in human skin.

EXPERIMENT 14. Reactions of the Digestive Tract in the Adults and Larvae of *Drosophila*

Animals and apparatus: Drosophila culture; yeast; Congo red; test tube; slide; strong lens or binocular microscope; ammonia; hydrochloric acid.

Fruit flies, especially while they are still in the larval stage, live mostly on the yeast cells that grow on rotting fruit. By feeding the insects with yeast stained with dyes that indicate the pH value, or actual acidity, of their surroundings, it can be shown that the various tracts of the gut differ in their reactions. A good demonstration can be given by boiling a quarter of an ounce of baker's yeast with 0.1 gms. of Congo red in a test tube half full of water; after boiling for a minute the red mass should be left to cool and settle and the water can then be poured off. Some of the sediment of colored yeast is poured on top of the medium in a culture of *Drosophila,* where the larvae feed

and where the adult flies can drink it. After ten minutes
or so, some of the larvae and flies have their guts filled
with yeast cells, and under a lens or a binocular microscope
it can be seen that in both cases long stretches in the first
third of the intestinal tract are bright blue; this indicates
that in this region there is a strongly acid reaction comparable to the acidity of human gastric juice, though probably in the insect gut it is phosphoric acid that is present
instead of hydrochloric. The rest of the intestine is seen to
be neutral or slightly alkaline in reaction, as it is filled with
shining-red yeast cells (Fig. 5). Similiar results are obtained with many other Diptera.

Fig. 5. Third instar larva of *Drosophila,* showing the
internal organs; the gut shows the red and blue areas,
indicating the regions of acid and alkaline reaction.
(Blue area is shown in black.)

The reactions of the colored yeast cell can be changed
outside the animal's body by putting a drop of the suspension of red cells on a slide and exposing it alternately
to the vapors of ammonia and hydrochloric acid.

CHAPTER III

Respiration

EXPERIMENT 15. Respiratory Movements in
Land Insects (36, 81)

Animals and apparatus: Stick insects; bees, beetles, or
moths; glass tube 5 mm. in diameter; grease or wax; projector.

One of the factors limiting the size of insects, as a class,
is the method of effecting gas exchange; for the oxygen
must diffuse through the tracheae instead of being carried
to the tissues by the hemoglobin of the blood. As the
amount of gas diffused through a tube in any unit of time
decreases with the length of the tube, it follows that the
size of insects is limited by the length of the tracheae.
However, there is an auxiliary mechanism, particularly in
larger insects, in the respiratory movements which are usually performed by the muscles of the abdomen. These
movements ventilate the main large tracheae in very much
the same way that the bellows of an accordion fill with air.
In some species the air passes in and out of a spiracle at
approximately the same rates, but in others, for instance
in *Diapheromera*, more air is taken in through one opening
of the tracheae system and more passes out at another; in
this way a weak air current is produced. This can be demonstrated in various ways. A stick insect is arranged in a
glass tube so that the air in front of the animal does not
communicate with the air behind it, except through the

tracheal system. This can be done by using grease or wax to block the lumen of the tube around the animal's body. If the inspiratory end of the tube is then dipped into water, so that a drop of water closes the lumen, the respiratory movements of the insect will make the drop move along the tube toward the animal in little jumps, provided that the tube is slightly tilted and not held vertically.

A more direct way of seeing respiratory movements is to bring an insect such as a bee, or a moth, or a large beetle, into the beam of a film projector and watch the shadow that it casts. The animal may be magnified up to ninety diameters and the movements can be watched easily and counted. Increase in temperature or a slight increase in the amount of carbon dioxide in the air will, as a rule, increase the frequency and amplitude of the respiratory movements, or even provoke them in individual insects which had previously shown none.

EXPERIMENT 16. Respiratory Movements in Water Insects

Animals and apparatus: Water beetles; May fly nymphs; damsel fly nymphs; two 2-lb. jam jars; thermometer; elodea; basin of cold water.

Aquatic insects and insect larvae can get their oxygen either from that dissolved in water or from the air. Many of the insects come to the surface periodically, and then a volume of air which they always carry on their bodies is brought into contact with the atmosphere so that an exchange of gases can take place. Different forms carry these air bubbles on different parts of the body; for instance, many beetles carry them under the wings, water boatmen on the ventral surface, and so on. If the water is very rich in oxygen, as it is in a river or in the presence of many

green algae on a bright day, enough oxygen diffuses from
the water into the "water lungs" of the insects to maintain
their metabolism, and they do not need to come to the surface for a long time. But in stagnant water or at night,
especially when it is warm, very little oxygen may be dissolved in the water, and then frequent visits to the surface
can be observed.

Many aquatic-insect larvae, for instance the nymphs of
May flies and damsel flies, do not carry air outside the
tracheal system and do not come to the surface to exchange
air; instead, they have so-called tracheal gills on the abdomen, which may be transformed legs or other appendages (Fig. 6). These are usually flat plates inside which

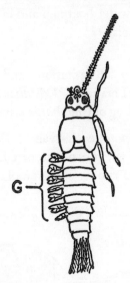

Fig. 6. Aquatic larva of the May fly, showing the mobile
abdominal tracheal gills on the left side.

are the fine branching tracheal capillaries filled with gas.
If the water is rich in oxygen, these gills may stay motionless or flap slowly, but in water which is poor in oxygen,

they will flap violently and thus cause a current continually bringing fresh water with fresh oxygen to the gills.

Both types of respiratory regulation can easily be shown by using two jam jars containing water in which there are different amounts of dissolved oxygen. One contains some fresh tap water, preferably with a bit of elodea or some other water plant in it. In the other, water is used which has been boiled for ten minutes so that it is practically free of gases. Both jars are put into a basin of cold water until they are at the same temperature, and then water insects of the types just mentioned are introduced into both of them. The differences in behavior can then be observed, and notes can be taken of frequency of surfacing in the beetles and water boatmen and of the movements of the gills in the others.

EXPERIMENT 17. Respiration and Tracheal Extension in the Larvae of *Eristalis* (Rat-tailed Larva) (25); Floating of *Chaoborus* Larvae.

Animals and apparatus: Larvae of *Eristalis* and *Chaoborus* (shown in Fig. 11); pupae of *Chaoborus;* tumbler; membrane, such as rubber sheet or bladder; string; *Drosophila* larvae.

The larvae of *Eristalis* (Fig. 7) are found in dirty water

Fig. 7. Rat-tailed larva of *Eristalis*.

and are remarkable for their great contractility. They are supplied with air by two long tracheae that communicate with the air by means of two spiracles at the posterior end of the body. The question arises as to how the two main tracheae change their length when the body of the larva changes. Tracheae are tubular invaginations of the skin in which the order of the layers is inverted. Thus, the mechanical elements which are on the outside of the skin of the insect's body form the inner layer in the tracheae; these elements are arranged either in rings or, more often, in spirals circling several times around the lumen of the trachea. Any change in the volume of such a tube must primarily affect its length; either the rings will move farther apart or closer together. In the larvae of *Eristalis,* they may be extended to twice the distance or contracted to half as the body stretches and contracts. These changes can be demonstrated in the following way. The larvae are put into a tumbler full of water which is covered by sliding a membrane, such as a piece of bladder or of rubber sheeting, across the top so that no air is included; under these conditions the larvae swim about at the surface just under the cover. If pressure is exerted on the covering membrane, the larvae sink owing to the reduction of the volume of air in the tracheae, and at the same time the animals get shorter. With a magnifying glass it can be seen that the shortened tracheae are fairly straight; in some other maggots, those of *Drosophila* for instance, the tracheae can be seen to become short and straight when the pressure is applied and to expand into curved forms when it is decreased, without there being any noticeable change in the length of the larval body.

The change in tracheal length is certainly an important means of changing the air in those insects which ventilate their tracheal system. In some other forms there appear to be tracheae with an elliptical or flat section which may change their volume by changing the area of the cross section of the lumen. In still other forms, in bees for instance, there are large air sacs around the brain, and in the abdomen, which act like a bellows by expanding and contracting and so changing the volume.

The floating balance in some other dipterous larvae which often populate standing fresh water can be demonstrated in the same way with a tumbler covered by a membrane. The larva of *Chaoborus* is a beautiful transparent animal which preys upon daphnids and is found motionless at various depths. It is kept floating by two pairs of tracheal sacs, each being kidney-shaped and rather heavily pigmented. If this larva is put into the tumbler, it will regulate its position after a few minutes; but when pressure is applied on the membrane, the insect will slowly sink to the bottom; and when the pressure is released, it will rise again. If very strong pressure is exerted, the movements may become very quick, and then violent swimming movements will occur. The anterior and posterior tracheal sacs are the only rudiments of the tracheal system in *Chaoborus* larvae, and the gas enclosed in them is completely cut off from the outside world. Similar developments are found in some parasitic larvae, whereas some of the insect parasites which attack other insects attach their tracheal systems to those of their hosts. The pupae of *Chaoborus*, which also occur in water and resemble mosquito pupae, can be made to sink or rise by changes of pressure in the same way.

EXPERIMENT 18. Actogram of a Stick Insect
(48, 65, 88)

Animals and apparatus: Adult stick insects; muslin cage; clockwork; metal cylinder; Meccano cogwheels; smoked paper; shellac; methyl alcohol; parts of actograph as described.

The motor activity of an insect during the twenty-four

hours can be demonstrated by means of a piece of apparatus working on the principle of a balance and called an actograph (Fig. 8). This consists primarily of a bar,

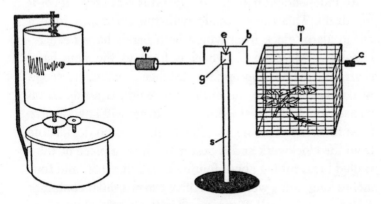

Fig. 8. Actograph for stick insects.

with a cage at one end in which the insect is contained, while the other end of the bar acts as a point writing on a slowly revolving smoked drum. By its movements the insect shifts the balance of the bar. The construction of such an actograph is quite simple, but it requires a certain amount of mechanical ability. The following parts are needed: The bar of the balance consists of about two feet of wire (16–18 standard wire gauge), bent as shown in Fig. 8 and pointed at the free end, which writes upon the drum; the point is slightly bent so that only the actual point itself rests on the drum. (Even better is to attach a paper point.) The bar is soldered to an edge (*e*), which rests in a grooved piece of metal (*g*), and this is mounted on a stand (*s*). A muslin cage (*m*), completely closed and containing a stick insect and some leaves, is hung on the end of the bar (*b*) and is held in position by a cork (*c*). A sliding weight (*w*) acts as a counterpoise to the cage.

Very slight changes in the distribution of weight, such as are caused by the insect's movements, will result in a swinging of the bar.

An independent part of the apparatus is the time-recording drum. This can be made with the clockwork from a cheap alarm clock from which both hands have been removed. A Meccano cogwheel is fixed to the hour-hand shaft, and at an appropriate distance from it, a second wheel, having twice the number of teeth, is arranged on an axis which carries the drum. The drum will now revolve once in twenty-four hours. The drum must be detachable from the clockwork and is best made from a piece of thin-walled brass tubing about four inches in diameter and four inches long; but a well-made coffee can or similar container may do equally well. It is covered with smooth white paper gummed into a ring and is blackened by means of a sooty flame, which can be produced by letting coal gas bubble through xylene before it enters a gas burner. (A candle will not produce such a good flame, though it may be possible to get enough soot from it to cover the drum.) The record is produced by letting the paper point on the end of the bar scrape the soot from the slowly revolving paper. Care must be taken to have the axis of the drum and the plane of movement of the balance absolutely vertical, so that the point is always in contact with the paper cylinder.

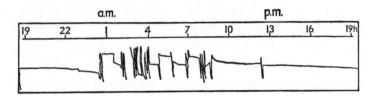

Fig. 9. Actogram showing the nocturnal activity of a stick insect. (In the original the line is white on a black ground.)

The time can be marked on the smoked paper by writing on it with any pointed implement; and the final record can be fixed after its removal from the drum by soaking it for a few seconds in a 10 per cent solution of shellac in methyl alcohol.

Stick insects will show a predominantly nocturnal peak of activity (Fig. 9), and this may continue for several nights even if they are kept in a completely dark room. But this rhythm of activity does not persist during continuous illumination.

Other insects, such as cockroaches, beetles, and bees, may be studied by similar methods.

CHAPTER IV

Locomotion

EXPERIMENT 19. Walking Order of a Stick
Insect's Legs (10)

Animals and apparatus: Adult stick insects.

The co-ordination of an animal's limbs when it is moving
has always proved a fascinating study. One of the first
scientific problems to be solved by cinematography was
whether a cantering horse ever has all four legs in the air
at the same time. The imaginary difficulties of a centipede
in walking are a standard joke; but it is still interesting
to discover how an insect walks, and even more interesting
to see how it modifies the limb co-ordination when one
or more of its legs are missing. Stick insects are very suitable
objects for such a study, as they move fairly slowly and
can also shed their legs easily by autotomy (Experiment
93), so that there is no need to cut them off to get results.

A complete stick insect can walk in various ways, but
usually it does so as follows: Two groups of legs move more
or less synchronously, the front and hind legs of one side,
together with the middle leg of the other side; e.g., the
left front and hind legs and the right middle leg will sup-
port the animal while the other three legs swing forward,
and when these are put down, the first three legs are moved
forward. If the observer is patient, occasionally other
modes of walking may be observed in an intact animal.

In any culture of *Diapheromera* there are always animals lacking one or more legs, so that their locomotion can

be studied without making them autotomize; but it is possible to lift an insect by one leg until it sheds it and then watch how it walks away. Only three possible situations are created by removing one leg, since it can only be a front or a middle or a hind leg (and it is immaterial whether it is on the right or the left side). But two legs can be removed in nine ways, and three legs in ten, and still the animal can walk fairly well except when all three legs are missing from the same side. No stick insect can walk with less than three legs. A further interesting point is that hardly any time is needed after the loss of one, two, or three legs to acquire the new method of progression; the insect can do it straightway. To study the movements of the legs, a series of simple line diagrams are required, of the type shown in Fig. 10, in which observations can be entered.

The remarkable adaptability shown in these experiments has been called plasticity of the nervous system; but it is more likely to be due to an inherent pattern of neural arrangement resulting in a new pattern of reflexes.

EXPERIMENT 20. Dynamic Maintenance of Swimming Position in *Chaoborus* Larva (60)

Animals and apparatus: Chaoborus larva; tumbler; alcohol, 10 per cent solution; sugar solution; pipette.

In Experiment 17, reference was made to the four gas-filled tracheal sacs in the larva of *Chaoborus*. These provide a hydrostatic mechanism by means of which the insect maintains its level while floating in the water. This mechanism acts rather slowly, and when the larva has caught a daphnid it sinks to the bottom for a considerable time; and for even longer it does not keep in its usual horizontal position. It was shown that great changes in

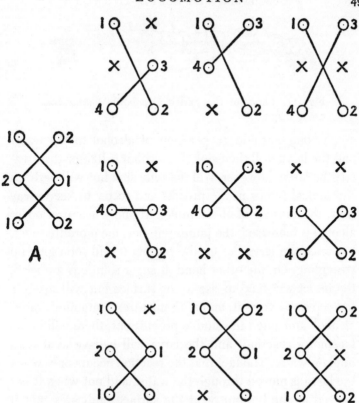

Fig. 10. Walking order of the legs of a stick insect, *Diapheromera femorata*. A. Co-ordination of legs in complete animal. B. The walking order in nine possible combinations of missing (*x*) and present (*o*) legs. (After von Buddenbrock)

pressure cause sudden motor reactions, which occur when the slowly working hydrostatic mechanism becomes inefficient.

It is easy to make a *Chaoborus* larva (Fig. 11) sink or rise by putting it into a liquid of lower or higher specific gravity. In this, one is greatly helped by the relative impermeability of the cuticle to many substances. For ex-

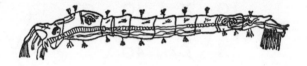

Fig. 11. Larva of the midge *Chaoborus plumicornis.*
10 × magn.

ample, one can add 10 per cent of alcohol to the water and the larva will then sink, for alcohol is lighter than water; the larva, however, will not only sink but will perform rhythmical jumps in the process and so try to keep away from the bottom of the tumbler. If the concentration of alcohol is increased, the jumps will become more frequent, but once the larva lies on the bottom it will soon give up struggling. On the other hand, if sugar solutions are used, the insect will tend to rise to the surface but will struggle to keep away from it; and with mixtures containing water, alcohol, and sugar in suitable proportions, there will be no locomotor reactions and the larva will behave as it does in plain water. The fact that the reaction occurs only when the larva is moved through the water, and not when it has arrived at the bottom or at the surface, indicates that it has a perception of currents and of the relative movements of body and water. This can also be shown by inducing the jumping reactions by passing a stream of water from a pipette over the insect.

EXPERIMENT 21. Wingbeat (15, 16, 17)

Animals and apparatus: Bees or flies; matchstick; glue; light paint; A.C. incandescent bulb, preferably vacuum; musical instruments; sooty paper (Experiment 18); wax; tuning fork with writing point made from straw or wire.

For a long time the flight of insects has excited great interest, which has not been diminished by the achievements of human flight; for the powers of many insects are far superior to those of man-made machines in many respects, though not of course in speed. Among other things, an insect can hover like a helicopter, then suddenly start away in almost any direction, and equally suddenly stop again; it can catch other insects during flight, it can mate in the air, and it can keep steady in relation to moving objects. Only some of the largest insects, such as some of the butterflies and moths, fly in a way which is comparable to the sailing and gliding of larger birds; the vast majority depend on a wingbeat of great velocity—usually exceeding the speed of the wingbeat of the hummingbirds.

The frequency of the wingbeat has excited the curiosity of physiologists for many years, and even now it is not clear how muscular contraction and relaxation can alternate so very quickly. There are many methods of determining the shape and frequency of the wingbeat, the most modern being by high-speed cinematography; but some of the simpler methods can give quite informative results. The shape of the wingbeat in a bee or a fly can be demonstrated by painting the tips of the insect's wings with some light paint and observing the movements of the wings in bright sunlight or in a bright illumination against a dark background. An insect can be made to "fly" on the spot by the method described in Experiment 40, by holding it with a matchstick glued to the back of the thorax; the track of the paint spots will follow a somewhat distorted figure of eight, and the whole performance will be seen to be more like the workings of an airscrew than the wingbeat of a bird or a bat. If the experiment is carried out in electric light supplied by an alternating current of a frequency of 60 cycles per second, the interference of this frequency with the frequency of the wingbeat can be shown by moving the insect more or less rapidly against a dark background; if the insect is moved regularly in a circle, one can see extreme wing positions which otherwise are invisible.

One way of estimating the frequency of wingbeat is by comparing the sound produced by flying insects with the sound of a piano or other musical instrument; but sometimes one may be badly led astray because of the harmonic overtones. Another method is to let the moving wings scratch on a revolving cylinder of sooty paper and count the marks made. For this purpose a match is stuck to the dorsal surface of a fly's thorax with glue, and when the insect is lifted so that its tarsi do not touch anything, it will "fly" for a considerable period (Experiment 40). In this state it can be used for recording the wingbeat frequency by holding it near a blackened drum (Experiment 18, the cogwheel of which has been disconnected from the clockwork so that the cylinder can rotate freely). If the speed of the sooty surface is known, or if simultaneous markings are recorded by a tuning fork of known frequency or vibration, the number of wingbeats per second can be estimated with a fair degree of accuracy; but it must be remembered that the friction of the scratching will decrease the speed to some extent.

The dependence of wingbeat on the load can be demonstrated by sticking a small amount of wax to the wing or by clipping both wings of a fly or both forewings of a bee; the presence of the wax will cause a decrease in frequency of wingbeat whereas the clipping will increase it.

EXPERIMENT 22. Artificial Expansion of the Wings of a Blowfly (37)

Animals and apparatus: Pupae of blowfly; test tube; siphon; stopper with two holes; glass tubing; rubber tubing; filter pump.

A newly hatched fly usually expands its wings in about half an hour, but the process can be speeded up artificially in a variety of ways. For instance, if the fly is exposed to an atmosphere rich in carbon dioxide a few minutes after its emergence from the pupa, the wings will expand in a few seconds. For this purpose a young blowfly is allowed to swallow some air and is then put into a test tube closed with a stopper in which there are two holes; through one of these there should be a glass tube connected with an inverted siphon such as is described on page 167. Carbon dioxide is now released from the siphon and penetrates very rapidly into the air inside the fly. As the other gases cannot escape out of the fly at the same speed, increased pressure results in the fly's body; this, in turn, expands the wings. A similar effect could be produced by sucking most of the air out of the test tube by attaching it to a filter pump; in this instance the air that had been swallowed by the fly would expand.

EXPERIMENT 23. Effect of Temperature on the Flight of Hawk Moths (26)

Animals and apparatus: Hawk moths; dark boxes; thermometer; dark room.

In Experiment 67 it is shown that hawk moths are not able to become air-borne as soon as the appropriate illumination is supplied but spend a little while fluttering their wings until the body temperature is sufficiently raised to allow of their flying. It can easily be shown that the length of the warming-up period depends upon the temperature at which the animal was kept before the experiment began.

To show this, two hawk moths of the same species are kept in dark boxes, one at room temperature and the other for at least half an hour at about 34°C. The second box can be kept under the experimenter's clothes or near a fire or an electric lamp to bring it to approximately the right temperature. If both the moths are then exposed to the same dim light, it will be found that the one kept at room temperature will flutter for some time before flying, while the other will be able to take flight at once.

EXPERIMENT 24. Production of Carbon Dioxide by a Flying Hawk Moth (56)

Animals and apparatus: Hawk moth; gallon bottle with fitting cork or stopper; dish containing 5 per cent barium hydroxide solution; dark room with red and yellow lamps.

Experiment 67 shows that a hawk moth can be induced to fly by exposing it to faint illumination after it has been kept in the dark. If it is made to fly in a large bottle, the carbon dioxide which is produced can be collected. A gallon bottle of white glass is coated with strips of newspaper about an inch wide and arranged about an inch apart, vertically and horizontally, so that a coarse network is formed (Fig. 12); this arrangement gives the moth a means of orienting itself and enables it to hover inside the bottle. The bottle is put in a dark room, and a small dish containing some filtered solution of barium hydroxide is carefully let down to stand at the bottom of the bottle. Using a red light, a hawk moth which has been kept in the dark for some hours is transferred to the bottom of the bottle and the bottle is stoppered. If the yellow light is then turned on, the moth will start vibrating its wings and will then begin to fly; after bumping several times against the glass walls, it may finally stay in mid-air in front of one of the strips of newspaper with its tail to the light for considerably more than a minute. After full lighting has been turned on, the moth will usually stop flying, and it can be seen that the surface of the baryta solution is covered with a thin film of barium carbonate; this is formed by the carbon dioxide produced by the moth com-

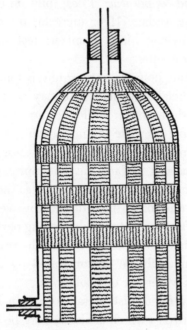

Fig. 12. Large aspirator covered with strips of news-paper, for flight of hawk moth.

bining with the barium hydroxide. If the moth were kept motionless in the bottle, it would take more than an hour to produce the same effect. Flight increases the amount of carbon dioxide produced by a hawk moth to roughly forty times the amount that is produced by the resting insect. That it is the carbon dioxide which produces the film of precipitate can be shown by breathing on a dish of baryta solution, when precisely the same effect will be obtained. (Care, of course, must be taken not to breathe on the baryta in the dish which is being used for the experiment.)

EXPERIMENT 25. Deposit of Droplets on an
Insect's Wings (21, 22)

Animals and apparatus: Flies; oily insecticide with
spray; 0.1 gms. sudan III or nigrosin; 0.1 gms. fuchsin,
eosin, or methylene blue; atomizer; test tubes; lens or
binocular microscope.

When a resting housefly or mosquito is sprayed with one
of the commercial insecticides, it may be struck by the
droplets from the atomizer while they are carried by the air
current, or while they are falling, or while they are being
carried by convection currents; in all these cases, every
part of the insect's surface has an approximately equal
chance of being hit. When the insect flies through a more
or less stable mist of an insecticide, however, the wings,
which are by far the most quickly moving part of the body,
collide with many more droplets than the rest of the body
does. This can easily be demonstrated by using colored
mists either in watery or oily solutions.

To prepare a dyed mist, a trace of sudan III (which is
red) or of nigrosin (which is black) may be added to one
of the oily commercial toxic sprays. Care should be taken
not to use this spray in a living room, as it would stain the
walls; but it can equally well be used in the open air owing
to the quick action of the commercial preparations; flies or
wasps visiting flowers may be sprayed, and they will die
in a few seconds and can then be collected. If it is more
convenient, fuchsin, eosin, or methylene blue can be dissolved in water and used in one of the sprays that are
commonly used by painters; but in this case, the insects
must be caught after they have flown through the colored
mist and then killed.

If an insect is inspected, either with a lens or a binocular microscope, after it has passed through the colored mist, it will be seen that there is more dye on the wings than on any other part of the body. The actual amounts can be estimated by a rough colorimetric method. To make this comparison, the wings should be cut from the dead insect and put into one test tube while the rest of the animal is put into another; both tubes should be filled to a depth of about an inch with some of the solvent used in making the spray. It will be found that the wings release much more of the dye than is released by all the rest of the body.

CHAPTER V

Cuticle and Epidermis

EXPERIMENT 26. Removal of Waxy Elements
from a Fly's Cuticle by Paraffin (52, 97)

Animals and apparatus: Flies; watch glass; paraffin;
methyl alcohol; lens or binocular microscope.

If a fly is submerged in water or alcohol it will not die
for a considerable time, as neither substance will permeate
the cuticle or easily infiltrate the tracheal system. Obviously, there is something which prevents these liquids
from coming into direct contact with the cell protoplasm
of the insect's epidermis. This something, which is most
probably a waxy layer, can be mechanically abraded
(Experiment 27), but it can also be removed chemically by
paraffin or by other hydrocarbons, some of which are
highly toxic to the insects.

A very striking demonstration of the breakdown of the
protective layer can be made as follows: An insect is submerged in a mixture of paraffin and methyl alcohol in a
watch glass and is then observed under a lens or a binocular microscope; after a few seconds hundreds and thousands of small bubbles can be seen coming out of the
cuticle and moving away from it, rapidly expanding as
they travel through the surrounding liquid. This phenomenon, which resembles the formation of carbon dioxide in a
glass of soda water, lasts for a few minutes and comes to an
end only when all the water has been drawn out of the

insect. The expanding bubbles are droplets of water which expand by the intake of alcohol, and they are visible because of the different optical density of paraffin and the water-alcohol mixture. If a vegetable oil is used to dissolve the wax layer instead of paraffin, it may take hours before a similar reaction is observed. A less spectacular way of showing the effect of removing the barrier from the insect's cuticle is to put a very small drop of paraffin on a fly's abdomen and then submerge the insect in methyl alcohol with an untreated fly for comparison. The first fly will die very much sooner from desiccation.

EXPERIMENT 27. Abrasion of the Wax Layer
on an Insect's Cuticle (97, 98)

Animals and apparatus: Housefly; beetle; test tubes; alumina powder; magnifying glass; emerald or sand paper; ammoniacal silver solution.

(NOTE. The silver solution is made by dissolving a small crystal of silver nitrate in about 20 cc. of water and adding ammonia to it until the cloudiness that appears at first dissolves again. The solution is poisonous, and dangerous if it gets into the eyes; it also stains the skin.)

The removal of the wax from an insect's cuticle by abrasion can be directly observed in bigger insects, such as cotton stainers (*Dysdercus*), under a binocular microscope, when the abrasions look rather like needle scratches on a candle. But in smaller insects the effect is best shown indirectly by removing the abrasive and then submerging the animal in an ammoniacal silver solution.

A fly or other small insect, preferably of a light color, is shaken in a test tube with some alumina powder; after ten minutes the animal is killed in the killing bottle, washed with water and a paintbrush, and then soaked in a weak ammoniacal silver solution. During immersion it should be kept in sunlight or near a bright lamp. After a few minutes one can see with a magnifying glass, or even with the naked eye, that parts of the cuticle become darker. In the case of a fly or any other insect that cleans its legs by rubbing them together, the legs will be the parts that are most affected. In an insect which tends to drag its abdomen along the ground, as some beetles do, the dark scratches will show there, after it has been left crawling on a sheet of emerald or sand paper.

The dark coloration is due to metallic silver being precipitated by the polyphenols, which are proteins found in the cuticle under the wax layer. Contact between the silver solution and the polyphenols can take place only where the wax has been removed; and the precipitation of metallic silver, which is in some ways comparable with the behavior of a photographic emulsion, can take place only in the light.

EXPERIMENT 28. Action of Inert Dusts on Insects (70, 97)

Animals and apparatus: Houseflies or fruit flies; maggots of fly; animal charcoal; killing bottle (page 169); siphon; test tubes.

Many insects die from loss of water, and older specimens are often found to be dry and shrunken; but considering the small size of the majority of insects, it is really remarkable that they do not dry up more quickly. A drop of water weighing one milligram disappears in a heated room in a few minutes; but a fruit fly of the same weight, of which about three quarters is water, does not die from desiccation for about a day, even if it does not receive any liquid. Most of the insect's protection against desiccation is provided by a very thin layer of wax on the surface of the cuticle; if this wax is removed, either mechanically or by a solvent, the insect will dry up very rapidly under ordinary conditions. A good way of removing the wax layer is by abrasion with chemically inert dusts (Experiment 27).

If houseflies, fruit flies, or mosquitoes are dusted with some finely ground animal charcoal, the black-coated insect will die in a few seconds or minutes, according to its size. A house spider will be affected in the same way. If the blackened animals are kept in an atmosphere saturated with water, however, they will live for many hours. Clearly, the deaths in the first case can be ascribed to the loss of water. The abrasive effect of the charcoal depends also on the active movements of the insects, for if they are sprinkled with the powdered charcoal when they have been previously immobilized by cold (Experiment 6), they will not die as long as they remain motionless. Immobilization can also be produced by using a killing bottle or by exposure to carbon dioxide from a siphon (page 167). The motionless pupae of a fly are not killed by the action of inert dusts, not only because they do not move but principally because there is a second waxy layer on the cuticle of the developing insect inside the pupal casing. Other chemically inert dusts, such as alumina, carborundum, and quartz powder, can also be used, but they act more slowly than charcoal.

Inert dusts are not only of direct use in the fight against many insect pests but they also act indirectly insofar as they facilitate the entry into the body of insecticides which would normally be kept out by the wax layer.

EXPERIMENT 29. Darkening of the *Tenebrio*
Beetle (85)

Animals and apparatus: Newly emerged *Tenebrio* beetles; Kipp's apparatus for making hydrogen; glass and
rubber tubing; metal clip; killing bottle (page 169).

The flour beetle *Tenebrio* derives its Latin name from
its dark color; when it emerges from the pupa it is quite
white, but at room temperature it will darken in about
two days. It is usually assumed that the color-giving substance, or chromogen, is absent in the fresh cuticle;
whereas the enzyme tyrosinase, which transforms chromogen into the dark melanin, is already present every-
where. After a few hours, however, the chromogen may
amount to 5 per cent of the cuticle. Dead *Tenebrio* beetles,
killed by heat or in a killing bottle, do not darken; nor does
the darkening proceed in a refrigerator or in the absence
of oxygen. To show that darkening does not take place in
the absence of oxygen, an experiment can be conducted
in an atmosphere of hydrogen produced from a Kipp's
apparatus (charged with zinc and sulphuric acid). A piece
of glass tubing half an inch in diameter, containing one
or more beetles (which are still light in color) enclosed
between loose cotton-wool stoppers, is connected to the
Kipp's apparatus by a piece of rubber tubing. The other
end of the glass tube is also fitted with about three inches
of rubber tubing; the latter is bent on itself and almost
closed with a metal clip. The hydrogen is passed through
the whole tube for several minutes and the metal clip is
then shut so that no more hydrogen can escape. After a
day or so no darkening of the beetles can be observed. But
when they are brought back into the air, they may still
recover, and if they do, they darken. No naked flame

should, of course, be brought near the Kipp's apparatus, since hydrogen forms a dangerously explosive mixture with air.

EXPERIMENT 30. Prevention of Hardening and Darkening of a Blowfly (37)

Animals and apparatus: Blowfly pupae in soil; flowerpot; glass disk.

The maggots of the blowfly *Calliphora* often burrow in the earth before pupation, and the emerging flies consequently have to crawl out of the soil. As a rule, they complete their inflation and the hardening and darkening of the cuticle in the first hour or so. If, however, the flies are prevented from leaving the soil, they will not harden and darken for many hours, though they will do so as soon as they are released.

This can be shown by putting a quantity of soil containing some of the pupae into a flower pot and covering the surface of the soil with a closely fitting glass disk. In these circumstances the flies will not harden and darken until the glass is removed and they are allowed to crawl out. It appears from this result not only that the changes in the cuticle are controlled by hormones and enzymes but that these, in turn, are also subject to some influence of the nervous system.

EXPERIMENT 31. Charging *Drosophila* Flies with Electricity

Animals and apparatus: Drosophila flies; etherizer; horn or plastic comb; test tube; cotton wool.

Small insects may be charged with electricity in several ways, and various interesting effects can then be observed.

One method is to comb the hair with a comb made of horn or plastic, until it crackles, and then bring the comb near to some etherized *Drosophila* flies. The insects will be attracted by it in the same way as are any other small bits of light matter; and after they have touched the comb, they will drop away again.

A more interesting method is to put some active *Drosophila* flies into a dry test tube closed with a plug of cotton wool and to rub the tube on a woolen sleeve. The flies will be jerked from wall to wall, and after some time will assume a sort of stupor, with the legs rather stretched and the wings crumpled and bending away from the glass wall.

The greater part of this reaction is a passive response to electrostatic forces, but the stupor may be caused by direct electrical action on the brain of the insect. It is probable, though it has not as yet actually been proved, that insects flying through the air may become electrically charged under certain conditions—for instance, if the air is dry and their speed is considerable. If this is so, electrostatic reactions may assume additional interest. Reactions to electricity may also occur in the neighborhood of high-tension cables.

EXPERIMENT 32. Conditions for the Formation of a Puparium (37, 40, 82)

Animals and apparatus: Larvae of houseflies, blowflies, or fruit flies; soda glass tubing ¼ inch in diameter; bunsen or alcohol burner; file for cutting glass; siphon; killing bottle (page 169); forceps; ether; test tube; filter paper.

The maggots of some of the Diptera form their pupae by a change in the cuticle, which is transformed from a soft and light-colored layer into a brittle brown case much shorter than the outstretched larva. Inside the puparium is formed a new cuticular layer, the real pupal cuticle, which remains quite thin and pale. The darkening and hardening of the puparium is regarded as a sort of tanning process, in which proteins containing polyphenols darken owing to oxidation and form loose compounds with the chitin. If this assumption is true, it should be possible to prevent the darkening by depriving the animal of oxygen or by poisoning the oxidizing enzymes. If the maggot of a housefly or a blowfly which has contracted in preparation for forming a pupa is enclosed in an atmosphere of nitrogen, hydrogen, or carbon dioxide, or indeed in any gas mixture not containing oxygen, it will not darken even after a long time; nor will it get hard. To demonstrate this, take some glass tubing which melts fairly readily and narrow it in one place by heating it in a bunsen or alcohol burner, pulling it at both ends while it is soft. After the tube has cooled down, a contracted maggot is put into it near the constriction; a second constriction is then made at least two inches away from the maggot, so that it does not get too hot while the glass is being heated. After cooling again, the tube is flushed through with carbon dioxide from an inverted siphon (page 167), and first the more distant constriction and then the nearer one is sealed off in the flame. After a day, when all the control flies will have pupated, the enclosed larva will be unchanged; though it may recover and pupate when air is admitted into the tube again.

Puparium formation can also be prevented by filling the tube with coal gas and sealing it. (There is little danger of explosion.) The carbon monoxide in the gas paralyzes the oxidizing enzymes, and so darkening is doubly prevented. Hydrocyanic acid also poisons these enzymes; hence larvae which are ready to pupate will also remain soft and light in color if they are put into a killing bottle, even in the presence of oxygen. That there are compounds present before pupation which are capable of forming dark pigments can be demonstrated in the following way: If the mature larvae of fruit flies are heavily etherized in a tube, they become quite black after a few hours; and their body juices will darken if they are injured, and the juice is sucked up with filter paper. Presumably, ether inhibits the action of some reducing enzyme, which in turn inhibits darkening.

A necessity for the tanning process is the presence in the body fluid of the so-called pupation hormone, which

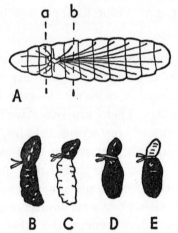

Fig. 13. A. Central nervous system of a maggot, showing the two places for ligature. B. Larva ligatured at level b after the critical period; both fragments pupated. C. Same ligature as in B, but applied before the critical period; darkening occurs only in the fragment containing the ganglion. D. Larva ligatured at level a after the critical period; both parts pupated. E. Same ligature as in D, but applied before the critical period; pupation only in the posterior part. In B and C the posterior parts are paralyzed, but not in D and E. (From Wigglesworth after Fraenkel)

is formed in a ductless gland—situated near the oesophagus and derived from the nervous system. If a full-grown larva (which, however, must not have contracted) is ligatured at about one third of its length away from the front end, the front part will in due course harden and darken. But the hind part will not. The ligature can easily be made by using a human hair and making a loop with a double knot. If the ligature is made too late—that is, when enough of the hormone has been released into the body fluid to cause pupation—pupa formation will occur in both parts of the body. (Fig. 13.)

EXPERIMENT 33. Color Change in Stick Insects (1, 54, 55)

Animals and apparatus: Two dark adult stick insects of the same color; cage with leaves; dark cage; thread.

The rapid changes of color which occur in the chameleon are proverbial. There are other well-known color adaptations in various crustaceans, fish, frogs, and indeed in many other animals; but among the insects there are very few which can change their colors quickly and reversibly. The stick insect *Diapheromera femorata* is one of these; it actually shows two sorts of change in color—one a slow cycle during development, the other rather faster. The young nymph hatching out of the egg is a tobacco-brown, dry-looking creature; but the second, third, and following instars are variable in color, including light-brown, dark-brown, and light-green individuals. This variation goes on into the adult stage. The difference between the green and the brown animals lies in the absence or presence of black pigment in the cylindrical epidermal cells.

The physiological or rapid color change can only be observed in the darkest adults (which will almost certainly all be females, as males occur only very rarely in captivity). If two equally dark specimens are selected, and one is put in the dark while the other is put into sunlight on a bit of leaf, after a few hours the one which has been in the dark will be much lighter than the one kept in the light on a dark background. Moisture also increases darkness, while exposure to dry conditions makes the animals lighter. Many other conditions operate in the same way, though to a lesser degree. Among other things, blackening parts of the eyes affects the color of the insect. By making a ligature with a piece of thread between the second and third pairs of legs, it can be shown that then only the front end of the animal will give a color response to environmental conditions, while the hind end will not. Elaborate experiments have shown that the change in color is brought about by a hormone produced in a ductless gland near the brain. In *Diapheromera femorata*, the pigment in the epidermal cells does not spread and contract in a plane parallel to the animal's surface (as it does in vertebrates and crustaceans) but fluctuates vertically—having accumulated nearer to the surface when the animal looks darker and having gone deeper when the color is lighter.

EXPERIMENT 34. Color Changes in the Pupae of *Pieris rapae* (28, 29)

Animals and apparatus: Adult caterpillars of cabbage white butterflies; boxes about the size of half-plate negative boxes ($7 \times 5 \times 1$ inches); glass plates; colored paper.

In Experiment 33, a quick, so-called physiological, color change was described in the stick insect *Diapheromera femorata*. This animal, in common with many other insects, also shows a slow, or morphological, change in color. This form of variation is most easily shown in the pupae of some pierid and vanessid butterflies, which vary according to the color of their surroundings.

The color of the pupa of the cabbage white butterfly *Pieris rapae* is made up of the green of some of the deeper tissues, a white pigment in the cells of the epidermis, and black spots of melanin in the cuticle. The variable factors are the black and white pigments, which are suppressed if the caterpillar is exposed to green, yellow, or orange light before it pupates. Pupae can be produced which are almost completely green, whereas checkered pupae are normally formed. Similar effects can be produced in the pupae of other cabbage whites and of vanessae, but here there seems to be a certain antagonism between the formation of the black and the white pigments. It seems that all the color adaptation is effected by means of the pupal eye.

For a demonstration, the pupae of the cabbage white butterfly are most conveniently used. The full-grown caterpillars usually migrate from the cabbage plants, and groups of half a dozen can be transferred to boxes lined with orange or black paper and covered with glass plates; after pupation, striking differences in color can be observed. Care should be taken to keep a bit of moist cotton wool in a corner of each box, and the boxes should be kept near a window or out of doors under shelter.

EXPERIMENT 35. Reactions of Pigments in the Wings of Butterflies and Moths (34)

Animals and apparatus: Butterflies and moths with yellow and red pigments; household ammonia; hydrochloric or glacial acetic acid.

The color in the wings of some butterflies is partly due to interference in the scales; and this iridescent physical color naturally changes with the angle of the beam of light and the direction from which it is observed. But most colors in Lepidoptera are due to pigments, which are present in the scales in the form of colored granules. Among these pigments two classes are most important: the brownish, blackish melanins and the reddish, yellowish, and even bluish pterins. The melanins are very similar to, and may be identical with, the substances that cause the pupae and the emerged insects to darken, and their formation can be interfered with in the way described in Experiment 32. The pterins, however, are quite different in chemical constitution and are related to some of the eye pigments in insects. Many pterins show striking color changes when they are exposed to strong acids and alkalis, and these changes can even be demonstrated in the dried-up wings of museum specimens. For instance, if the orange parts of the wings of the great tiger moth, *Arctia caja*, are exposed to the vapors of household ammonia, they become redder; whereas the vapors of dilute hydrochloric acid or strong acetic acid will turn the color to a light yellow, or perhaps even to green or blue. Both discolorations disappear when the vapors of the ammonia or acid evaporate; and as the wings are not damaged by the operation, specimens in a collection can safely be treated in this way, and considerable information can be gained about the nature and distribution of the pterins in the Lepidoptera.

CHAPTER VI

Mechanical Senses

EXPERIMENT 36. Mechanical Stimulation of
Caterpillars (41)

Animals and apparatus: Caterpillars; food plants; bristle
glued to handle; thread glued to handle; pencil; glass rod
2 mm. in diameter; needle; ice; thermometer.

Caterpillars provide good material for giving a demonstration of response to mechanical stimuli. The huge
caterpillars of the *Cecropia* moth (*Platysomia cecropia*)
are particularly suitable, but those of some of the whites
(*Pieris*), and of many others, are almost as good. Two
kinds of reactions, as a rule, can be observed: responses to
a slight touch, which is usually received by hairs; and responses to a stronger impact, which is presumably received
by the epidermis and the nerve system underneath. For the
slight touch, a bristle, or a piece of thread, four millimeters
long glued to a short handle can be used. For the stronger
stimulus, a sharpened pencil can be used, or a short glass
rod made by heating a piece of glass rod two millimeters
in diameter in a flame and pulling it out to about one millimeter in thickness (the end of the thin part when it has
been broken can be rounded in a flame). The caterpillars
should be tested on their appropriate food plants. As a rule,
a light touch elicits two kinds of reaction: if the thorax is
touched with a bristle, the anterior end of the body moves
away from the instrument; but if the abdomen is touched,
the anterior end moves toward the stimulus whether it is

applied on the animal's back or side. If attention is paid to the exact point of touch, it may be seen in some species that certain hairs are particularly susceptible to the tactile stimuli, whereas other parts of the epidermis may prove indifferent. Another useful observation can be made on habituation, for as a rule caterpillars will not respond so well to a second touch, and perhaps not at all to a third. The response is quite different in the case of the stronger mechanical stimulus produced by the pencil or glass rod. This will result, not in any reaction of the anterior end of the body, but in the flight of the entire animal. Especially strong reactions can be produced by gentle pricking with a sharp needle.

In some species of caterpillars a similar technique can be used to produce heat reactions. This can be done by touching the animals with pointed bits of dry ice, or with the bulb of a heated thermometer, and by carefully comparing the ensuing reactions with those obtained from a similar touch with an instrument at room temperature.

EXPERIMENT 37. Reaction of Caterpillars to Vibration (12)

Animals: Yellow-necked caterpillars on food plant.

Many caterpillars (e.g., *Datana ministra,* the yellow-necked caterpillar, and *Stauropus fagi*), when they are attacked, put their heads and tails up as if they were preparing to defend themselves. This reaction can be very beautifully shown by gently shaking the plants on which the caterpillars are feeding.

EXPERIMENT 38. Thigmotaxis of the Earwig
(95, 96)

Animals and apparatus: Earwigs; jam jar; lamp.

Some insects are inhibited in their movements by contact
with solid surfaces, especially when the contacts are not
confined only to the ventral surface. Most likely this reaction has a protective value by keeping the animal in
cracks and other sheltered places. In addition to this im-
mobilizing effect, some insects are even induced to increase
the area of contact between the body and its surroundings,
so that they actively move into cracks and hollows and
then remain immobilized there. Earwigs, for instance,
when they are put into a jam jar where the bottom of the
jar makes an acute angle with the sides, will press themselves tightly into the gutter and remain there even when
it is brightly illuminated, although under normal circumstances they run away from the light. (Fig. 14.)

Fig. 14. Thigmotaxis of an earwig squeezing itself into
the angle at the bottom of a jam jar. (After Weyrauch)

EXPERIMENT 39. Avoiding Reactions in the
Whirligig *Gyrinus* (31, 32)

Animals and apparatus: Whirligigs; aquarium; cloth;
paraffin wax; glass plate.

Water beetles swimming hurriedly on the surface of a

pond do not bump into each other; nor do they touch any other objects, such as reeds. In an aquarium, too, they cleverly avoid each other, as well as the walls of the vessel. It might be thought that this is a consequence of the beetles' seeing each other; but they avoid each other equally well if the aquarium is illuminated only by the red light of a darkroom lamp—to which light the beetles do not react. On the other hand, they do collide if all dust is removed from the surface of the water; and they bump against the glass walls when the aquarium is coated inside with paraffin wax so that the water meniscus disappears, or rather becomes negative. The most likely explanation of this behavior would be that a beetle perceives the movement of particles on the water surface caused by another beetle or by the reflection from the wall of the vibrations of its own movements. The organ perceiving the vibrations may be Johnston's organ—a complex structure mainly composed of tactile hairs. For if the antennae are cut between the first and second segments, and Johnston's organs, which are localized in the second segment, are thus removed, the beetles no longer avoid each other and collisions occur. The aquarium walls need be paraffined only near the edge, but they must be quite dry when the melted paraffin is applied. The surface of the water in a vessel can be cleared of dust and other solid particles by skimming it several times with the sharp edge of a glass plate.

EXPERIMENT 40. Tarsal Inhibition in the Fly (35)

Animals and apparatus: Flies; matches; wax.

Many insects, for instance some of the water beetles, have an unusually great variety of movements. They may walk, jump, swim, and fly—and each of these activities is a very complex performance which takes place only under certain conditions. Some of the conditions which are necessary for flight in certain insects, namely, temperature and light, are given in Experiments 23 and 67. Another condition which is necessary for many insects is that the tarsi must not be in contact with a solid object; by this means the insect is safeguarded from ceasing to fly while it is still in mid-air.

The tarsal inhibition of a fly can be removed in various ways. For example, it has been shown that prolonged flight can be induced by cutting off the tarsi. A simpler experiment is to throw a fly or bee into the air. A healthy specimen will rarely fall but will immediately fly away; many beetles, however, under such treatment, will not fly. A more controlled experiment can be made on many species of dragonflies, flies, and wasps. All that is needed is a matchstick pointed at one end and fixed with a little wax to the dorsal side of the thorax and abdomen of the insect. By this means the insect can be lifted from the surface on which the tarsi are resting and held suspended in the air. A *Drosophila* will "fly" until it is exhausted if the tarsi are prevented from making contact with a solid surface, and so will many other insects. Other species will fly only for a limited time, while many beetles will not spread their wings at all under these conditions. If contact of the tarsi with a solid is restored, the flying insect promptly stops beating its wings; but the procedure can be repeated.

EXPERIMENT 41. Inhibition of the Turning Reflex in Beetles by a Ball of Cotton Wool (12)

Animals and apparatus: Large beetle; caterpillar; cotton wool; matchstick.

Most animals have one or more natural postures. For instance, a very common normal posture is for the animal to be oriented with the ventral side to the substratum and the back upward. This posture may be induced by various stimuli—such as light, or mechanical contact with the substratum. If such an animal is turned on its back, be it a starfish, a cat, or an insect, it will turn over after a short time; and only a few organisms, such as tortoises or large beetles, have any difficulty in getting back onto their feet. In many large beetles the turning attempts consist in a rather futile wriggling of the legs, which may or may not result in one of the legs getting a hold somewhere and so enabling the beetle to turn over. By giving a beetle which is lying on its back a little ball of cotton wool to play with, its struggling can be checked for a long time. The contact of the tarsi with the relatively solid material apparently inhibits the turning movements. Similar reactions can be seen in caterpillars by giving them some elongated object, for instance a bit of stick, to hold when they are lying on their backs.

EXPERIMENT 42. Falling Reflex in Stick Insects (13)

Animals and apparatus: Stick insects; harvest spiders; etherizer; cardboard; insect needles.

Since the time of Aristotle, it has been known that a cat falling from a height always lands on its feet; and cinematography has revealed the complicated neuromuscular reactions which culminate in this result. It is not so widely known that similar effects can be observed in arthropods.

If a stick insect, preferably not an adult, falls from a height of not less than six inches, it will invariably alight on its legs; and the same thing happens when it is thrown into the air. The best way to throw the insect is to put it on a piece of flexible cardboard and then give a sharp flip to the underside of the card. A dead insect or one which has been narcotized will not always land on its legs but may come down in a variety of other positions. But a dead animal can be made to land with the back uppermost if it is fixed in position with the back hollowed, the antennae slightly raised and bent backward, and the legs in the normal standing position. Slow-motion pictures show that this is the attitude assumed by the living animal while falling. It is induced by the lack of contact between the tarsi and any solid object. Tarsal contact can be avoided for a slightly longer time by balancing a stick insect on two insect needles in such a way that the body is supported in front of and behind the middle pair of legs; it will then assume the attitude which has just been described.

A falling reflex can also be seen in the harvest spider (Phalangida). Aquatic arthropods, such as the larvae of water beetles and some dragonflies, or the adult crayfishes and shrimps, also assume similar postures when they sink to the bottom of the water.

EXPERIMENT 43. Catalepsy in Stick Insects (86)

Animals and apparatus: Stick insects; etherizer.

Since the time of Mesmer, various phenomena in animals have been described under the general name of animal hypnosis. The immobilization of chickens and other domestic animals, and of crayfish, come under this head. But it is more usual nowadays to apply the name catalepsy to all these phenomena.

Anyone who has kept stick insects knows that they are often found motionless in various odd positions (Fig. 15).

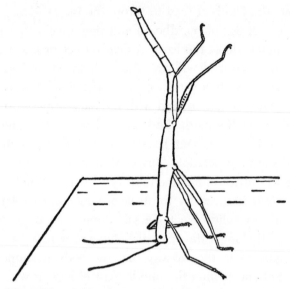

Fig. 15. Cataleptic stick insect put on its head and remaining there. (After Schmidt)

For instance, they may be extended with the antennae and the first pair of legs stretched forward and the other legs backward, thus forming a single stick; or the antennae and front legs may be held in this position while the animal stands on the back legs; and so on. Another unusual type of behavior may often be observed, particularly in the instars. This is a rocking movement persisting for many minutes, when the animal sways from left to right and back from right to left. In overcrowded cages, various instars may be found standing on each other and rocking in the most curious way. This characteristic movement has no apparent purpose, but seems to be merely a neuro-muscular hitch comparable to the cataleptic immobilization. It is quite distinct from the co-ordinated walking described in Experiment 19 and may be followed or preceded by it.

Catalepsy in an adult stick insect can easily be produced by rolling it very gently with two fingers on a level surface. The catalepsy can be broken by heat, or by chemicals such as ammonia, and by other stimuli (Experiment 65), such as gently pinching it near its hind end, where a large nerve center is found in the abdominal chain.

Catalepsy is not merely a lack of movement; it involves the simultaneous action of antagonistic muscles, resulting in considerable rigidity of the limbs. This can easily be demonstrated by trying to displace them with the finger. Etherized insects do not assume cataleptic positions but become completely limp.

Similar immobilization is found in many beetles and other insects, where it is often described as "feigning death" and is assumed to have a protective value by hiding the motionless insect from predators which react to movement.

EXPERIMENT 44. Immobilization of a Dragonfly (12)

Animals and apparatus: Dragonfly; black paint; brush; etherizer.

In Experiments 66 and 67, the influence of the eyes and of light on locomotion are demonstrated; and in Experiment 6, the immobilization of various insects has been described. It is possible to effect, or rather to prolong, immobilization by painting an insect's eyes. The dragonfly *Aeschna constrictor* will sometimes remain lying on its back on a table when it is gently held there; but if its eyes and ocelli are painted black in the way described in Experiment 66, the time of immobilization may be increased up to sixty times as long. Even individuals which prove refractory to immobilization as long as they can see may show the reaction clearly under these conditions.

EXPERIMENT 45. Reactions to Water Currents
by the Larvae of the Dragonfly *Aeschna* (91)

Animals and apparatus: Aeschna larvae (Fig. 16);
aquarium; glass rod 3 inches long; acetone glue; filter
paper for drying larva; pair of fine scissors; 2 feet of rubber
tubing and tapering glass tube leading from tap or ele-
vated vessel to produce water current.

Fig. 16. Larva of the dragonfly *Aeschna*.

Water currents cannot be perceived unless the water
moves relatively to the body. Therefore, an orientation or
any other reaction to streaming water can only be ex-
pected either in an insect which is holding tightly to the
substratum or in actively swimming animals. In the latter
case, no orientation to the direction of an external current
can be observed, but a definite posture frequently occurs
which usually facilitates motion; for instance, the larvae
of *Aeschna*, while swimming, characteristically hold their
legs backward and closely applied to the body, thus de-
creasing resistance. If the thorax of an *Aeschna* larva is
glued to a glass rod, and the animal is observed "swimming" on the spot, the legs are seen to be drawn tight

during expiration (the animal moves by the expiratory movement of the abdominal gills); but during inspiration they are stretched out in the normal way. Amputation of the antennae abolishes the reaction. The stimulus altering the posture thus acts by the antennae perceiving the currents. If a weak current of water is directed against the head of the fixed intact larva, adduction of the legs results. The animal's thorax must be carefully dried with filter paper before the rod is glued to it.

EXPERIMENT 46. Anemotaxis in Insects (66)

Apparatus: Narrow rubber tubing.

Horses can often be seen turning their tails to a strong wind, especially if it is raining. Other herbivorous and carnivorous animals are known to face the wind on many occasions; and so do some insects, although this is not very conspicuous. A demonstration of this anemotaxis can be given on a windowpane in summer by blowing through a piece of thin rubber tubing at some of the small Diptera and aphids which can be found crawling there. In many cases, if an air stream is directed against such an insect, it will be seen to turn toward the current of air when the force is just not strong enough to carry it away. Actually, this is a semimechanical reaction, consisting of an interaction between the holding-on animal and the air which tries to drag it away. It is in this way comparable with the negative geotaxis which frequently makes animals crawl upward and which in insects is most likely caused by the weight of the body dragging it downward and the animal itself struggling against the force.

EXPERIMENT 47. Catching a Fly (12, 24)

It is not so easy as may appear to catch a fly when it is sitting on a wall or any other plane surface. The technique is to get near it from behind with the hollowed hand and then very suddenly to move the hand along the plane and close it; the fly is then caught by the skilled operator just as it is taking off. As it takes off by jumping backward at an angle of about 60 degrees, it very often lands in the hollowed hand. There was some controversy on whether the shadow or the air currents generated by the moving hand cause the fly to take off. If the shadow of a hand is cast on a fly when the hand itself is moved at some distance from the wall, the insect will not always react. If (Experiment 46) the end of a piece of rubber tubing is very gently brought close to the fly so that it is not disturbed and then air is blown through the motionless tubing, the fly will turn and face the current, but will not take off, unless blown away. A housefly with its eyes painted black (Experiment 66) will not take off even in a very strong air current. On the other hand, flies sitting under a glass cloche will in suitable light conditions react to the movements of a hand near by.

It thus appears that the flight reactions of houseflies are visually controlled and not elicited by air currents. Previous escapes can to some extent modify the reactions.

EXPERIMENT 48. Flight from a Tuning Fork by the Pig Louse, *Haematopinus suis* (93)

Animals and apparatus: Haematopinus suis; tuning fork.
Many ectoparasites have developed special mechanisms to protect themselves against scratching and other mechanical devices which the hosts use in their efforts to

dislodge their parasites. This can easily be demonstrated in *Haematopinus suis*, which is a fairly big insect living on the domestic pig. If the insects are removed from the pig's skin and put onto a piece of cloth on a table, they will very often become almost motionless, and it will be difficult to rouse them. In all probability, this immobilization very often saves them from detection and consequent destruction. If, however, a tuning fork is struck and set upon the table near them while it is still vibrating, they will immediately run away from the source of the vibrations. This experiment should be conducted in a warm room.

EXPERIMENT 49. Reactions to Loud Sounds (84)

Animals and apparatus: Aquarium with *Dytiscus;* whistles.

It is often reported, and indeed it can often be observed if one keeps a lookout for it, that swarms of midges or of May flies are greatly disturbed by the whistle of a railway engine some distance away; the insects seem to tumble in all directions. An analysis of this phenomenon has not yet been undertaken, but a similar reaction can be obtained by using an aquarium in which there are water beetles of the genus *Dytiscus* and by blowing a whistle near it. Even if the whistle is sounded as much as two yards away from the aquarium, so that there is no visible movement of the water, it may cause very violent and apparently undirected flight reactions. In this experiment, whistles of different pitch are found to be differently effective, and varying results can be obtained by blowing the whistles at varying distances.

EXPERIMENT 50. Hearing of Field Crickets
(*Gryllus assimilis*) (83)

Animals and apparatus: Gryllus assimilis, male and female; a species of *Melanoplus,* two males; wire cage as described; telephone; Galton whistle.

The hearing of insects is still rather a controversial subject, although there is no doubt that some of them can not only hear but can also produce sounds. The particular sound made by angry bees is well known to beekeepers, and so is the noise made by the young queens; but it has only very recently been proved that bees, especially drones, react to low tones.

Sense organs of various kinds, which for a long time have been assumed to be acoustic receptors, have been found on the bodies and legs of many grasshoppers, crickets, and cicadas (Fig. 17). The investigation of hearing in insects

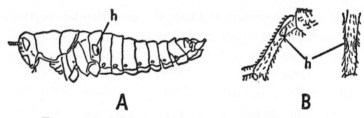

A   B

Fig. 17. A. Side view of a short-horned grasshopper, showing the tympanal organ of hearing, *h.* B. Organs on the front tibia of a cricket.

is to a large extent based on Regen's researches. With grasshoppers and crickets, two simple methods are available: one depends on the habit of rival males of chirping alternately; and the other on the observation of the tracks of female crickets when they are attracted by the chirping of a male.

To investigate the latter case, a pair of common field crickets can be caught without much difficulty. The male is put into a wire cage about three inches square made with a very fine-meshed netting, which renders the insect almost invisible; in addition, one side of the cage is covered with paper. Meanwhile, the female is kept in another box. The male in his cage is put on a table and, when he starts stridulating, the female is released from her box on the same table so that the paper wall is between her and the male. She will then approach him in an almost straight line, although he is completely hidden from her by the paper wall. If the male stops stridulating during the female's advance, she becomes uncertain in her course. She will not be able to find the male either if the sound-producing edges of his legs are injured or if her tympanal organs are destroyed. If the experimenter is a radio amateur, an even more striking demonstration can be given by transmitting the sounds made by the male into another room by telephone. The female will then be attracted to the telephone.

The second proof of the ability of an insect to hear can be obtained by using two males of the same orthopteran species, e.g., grasshoppers of the same species in the genus *Melanoplus*. In this species, a male chirps for long periods punctuated by pauses. If two males are kept near each other, one will chirp when the other stops and vice versa, though the alternation will not be absolutely regular. Notes can be taken using simple parallel lines to indicate alternate and simultaneous sound production, and it will be found that the alternation is much too frequent to be due to mere chance. The conclusion follows that one animal must be able to hear the other. In this case, too, destruction in one or both of the grasshoppers of the tympanal organs on the femora will upset the reaction, and the alternation will then occur only by chance.

In the open, the alternation of chirping, not only of two but of many grasshoppers, can be clearly heard by lying down in the grass of a meadow in summer and by focusing one's attention on the music of single grasshoppers.

The acoustic reactions of insects do not seem to be dependent so much on the primary pitch of the chirping as on more complex rhythms of a much lower frequency, such as are produced by voicing an *s*. By producing a high-pitched *s* with a Galton whistle, a male *Thamnotrizon* may be induced to alternate his note in a duet with the sound of the whistle.

Investigation of the hearing and sound production can be also pursued by means of a tape recorder.

CHAPTER VII

Chemical Senses

EXPERIMENT 51. Water Perception in Bees
(50)

Animals and apparatus: Trained bees; two milk bottles; wire gauze.

Bees can be used to demonstrate the attraction of insects to water. On a hot day, bees which have been trained to come to a table (Experiment 84) will gather on top of a milk bottle which has been half filled with water and closed with a piece of wire gauze. On a similar milk bottle, which is also closed with wire gauze but which is empty, no bees, or very few, will collect.

EXPERIMENT 52. Attraction of the Stick Insect to Water

Animals and apparatus: Stick insects, nymphs and adults; glass pipette; quinine, 1 per cent solution; hydrochloric acid; ammonia; cane sugar, 5 per cent solution.

It is well known that many insects drink water and must, therefore, be able to find it, but it is difficult to demonstrate how they find it and what sense organs they use in doing so. It can be demonstrated relatively easily, however, with stick insects, both in the adult and in the immature stages. For instance, the first instar, which may still carry the eggshell about with it, is often for a day or two without food; and if a small drop of water is put on the table beside it, near its head, it will start characteristic movements with its antennae and finally bend its forelegs and drink. Even more satisfactory results are obtained with adults, as the movements of their mouth parts can be seen very much better. As mentioned on page 173, stick insects kept on leaves or grass should be given a good spray daily; and when this is done, most of them can be seen drinking. But for a demonstration it is best to take out one individual just before spraying—i.e., a day after it has last been sprayed—and bring the opening of a glass pipette filled with water to within about one centimeter of its mouth. Very soon the animal will be seen to drink. If the water is held near the antennae, their movements may indicate water perception, and the insect may begin moving until it can reach the water with its mouth. Thus, two types of perception of water can be distinguished: one from a distance, which is probably due to the antennae; and the other at close range, which is probably effected by organs on the mouth parts.

This method can also be used to demonstrate the perception of dissolved substances, both volatile and non-volatile. Stick insects will turn away from a drop of hydrochloric acid or ammonia long before it gets into the region of the mouth; but they will taste a 1 per cent solution of a quinine salt, although they then refuse to drink it; they will, however, drink from a 5 per cent sugar solution.

EXPERIMENT 53. Orientation of *Drosophila melanogaster* by Smell (33)

Animals and apparatus: Drosophila flies or blowflies; three glass test tubes; glass T tube; three corks with single holes, one cork with two holes; rubber tubing; fruit or fly food; fish or meat.

Many insects find their food or their mates by sense of smell. This can be shown by using a simple piece of apparatus called an olfactometer. This can easily be made with three of the test tubes that are used in the culture of *Drosophila;* each should be fitted with a cork with a hole in it, through which the arms of a glass T tube can be inserted (Fig. 18). A few dozen *Drosophilae* are shaken into

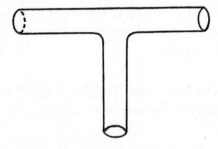

Fig. 18. T-shaped piece of glass tubing, which can be used as an olfactometer.

the empty test tube 1, which is immediately corked and so connected with the other two test tubes by means of the T tube. Test tube 2 contains a bit of moist filter paper; and in test tube 3 there is a small bit of pear or banana or a little fermenting fly food. The whole apparatus is put away in a lightproof box, and after an hour the number of flies in each of the three test tubes are counted; there should be most in the test tube containing the food. A similar arrangement on a rather larger scale can be used for blowflies, but a bit of fish or meat (preferably cooked) must be used instead of the fermenting fruit or fly food.

Another and more direct way of showing attraction by smell is to use only one test tube fitted with a stopper with two holes. This test tube contains the fruit or fly food, and two glass tubes pass through the holes in the stopper. Air is gently blown in at one glass tube by means of a piece of rubber tubing, and the air current comes out of the other carrying with it the smell of the food material. This emerging air is directed against some *Drosophila* flies which have been deprived of their wings during previous etherization. These flies will react very definitely, moving against the scented air current rapidly and accurately. The reaction is quite different in appearance from the reaction to an unscented air current (Experiment 46), and it is also different from the wind reactions obtained with some species of *Drosophila*.

EXPERIMENT 54. The Threshold for Sugar of the Tarsal Taste Organs of Butterflies (76, 77, 78, 94)

Animals and apparatus: Vanessa butterfly; house- or blowflies; cardboard strips; sugar solutions; test tubes; paintbrush; quinine; salt.

Most of the organs which respond to chemical stimuli in insects are situated on the mouth parts, the tarsi, and the antennae. In a variety of butterflies and flies, in the honey-bee, and in many other insects, touching the tarsi of the front legs with a sugar solution leads to an extrusion of the proboscis. This can be well demonstrated in butterflies of the genus *Vanessa,* such as the painted lady butterfly. The folded wings of the butterfly are held between two strips of cardboard half an inch wide, so that the legs can rest on the table. The strips of cardboard for this purpose can be held between the leaves of an upright book or with a clothespin (Fig. 19). Water and sugar solutions of increasing concentrations are arranged in a set of test tubes, and one of the front legs of the insect is touched with a paintbrush moistened with the solution. When plain water is used, there will be no reaction from the proboscis. But a sugar solution containing about M/50 sugar, which is just sweet to human taste, will cause the proboscis to be extended; so will any stronger solution. If the butterfly has been starved of sugar for a day, it will even extend the

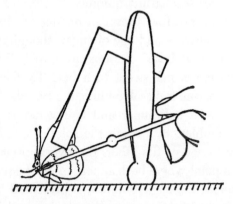

Fig. 19. Holder for a butterfly, to facilitate testing the chemical sense. (After Minnich)

proboscis after the tarsi have been touched with a very weak solution containing only 1/100 of the M/50 solution that was used before. This shows that the absolute concentrations which are effective vary with the condition of the individual butterfly; thresholds also differ with the species. Usually sucrose is the most effective of all the sugars. If a minute amount of quinine is added to a sugar solution, no response will be observed; but 4 per cent salt solution is not repellent. In the case of very thirsty butterflies, distilled water may be taken.

Similar experiments are possible with house- or blowflies with their wings glued to rods: movements of the proboscis can be elicited from the proboscis or the front tarsi.

EXPERIMENT 55. Is Saccharine Sweet to a
Bee? (44)

Animals and apparatus: Marked bees; petri dishes;
tumblers; sugar; saccharine; quinine.

Many people say that they can distinguish between a
solution of saccharine and one of sugar, though most people will agree that both solutions are sweet. But apparently saccharine is not sweet to a bee. To show this, a
tablet of saccharine is dissolved in half a tumbler of water,
and a solution of half sugar and half water is prepared
in another tumbler. By tasting the solutions, and adding
more water to one or the other, the two solutions can be
brought to a point where both appear to be of equal sweet-
ness. If some of the sugar solution is presented in a petri
dish to marked bees (Experiment 101), they will feed hap-
pily. But if a petri dish containing some of the saccharine
solution is substituted for the sugar, the bees will not drink
for the usual minute or so but will fly away disappointed.
It is clear that they can distinguish between sugar and
saccharine.

If access can be had to other kinds of sugars and sweet-
ening substances, interesting information can be obtained
about their action on the chemical sense of bees. As far
as the sugars are concerned, the results obtained with bees
will follow closely the responses given by human beings
for the same substances. Bees, moreover, are repelled by
strong bitter tastes and will refuse syrup to which quinine
has been added.

EXPERIMENT 56. Discrimination between
More or Less Sweet Sugar Solutions and Memory in Bees (18)

Animals and apparatus: Bees; ten petri dishes; sugar
solutions.

It has been shown that bees can distinguish between
higher and lower concentrations of sugar, and this can be
demonstrated in the following way. Ten petri dishes are
set out on a lawn in two rows, with five dishes in each row,
each dish being about a yard away from its neighbors.
Five of the dishes, chosen at random, are supplied with a
solution of one part of sugar to two parts of water; while
the others contain a solution of one part of sugar in ten
parts of water. Bees are attracted to the dishes in the way
described in Experiment 84, and the time is awaited when
all the syrup in all the dishes has been licked away and
the bees are searching in all of them for more. At this point
the dishes are refilled with the same solutions, and the
whole procedure may be repeated two or three times.
Finally, when most of the bees have gone away after the
last dish has been emptied, all the dishes are refilled with
a sugar solution in which there is one part of sugar in three
parts of water. This can be done on the following day if
necessary. After a time the number of bees sitting on the
different dishes are counted, and it will be found that the
dishes which originally contained the sweeter solution will
have attracted more bees than the others. This effect may
persist over several days, but it will sometimes be complicated by local or accidental factors favoring a particular
dish, such as differences in the quantity of syrup or the
chances of a first visit.

EXPERIMENT 57. Producing an Artificial Ant
Route with Traces of Formic Acid (12)

Animals and apparatus: Ants' nest; formic acid, ½ per
cent solution.

As a rule, ants march along fairly well-defined routes,
which are marked by traces of formic acid left behind by
the insects as they crawl. This doubtless facilitates the
orientation of the ants to the nest and also helps with the
location of food.

It is possible to imitate this effect by painting a route
across the ground or along plants in the neighborhood
of an ants' nest with very dilute formic acid. It will be
seen that the trail will be eagerly followed by large numbers of ants.

EXPERIMENT 58. Training Bees to Smells and
Exciting Bees in a Hive (43, 45)

Animals and apparatus: Bees; materials for marking as
in Experiment 101; blue, yellow, and green paper; petri
dishes; syrup of 50 per cent sugar; orange scent.

The way in which a bee which has found a rich source of
nectar communicates this information to her sisters has
puzzled beekeepers and naturalists for a long time. The
explanation, however, is really quite simple; and any fairy
tales about one bee telling the others, or leading the others
to a locality, can be discounted. When a bee returns to the
hive with her stomach filled with honey or nectar, she starts
dancing on the combs in a characteristic way, beating her
wings and thus spreading the smell of the flower which
clings to her body. The other bees become interested by
the dance and go searching for that particular smell. That

it is mainly the smell which serves as a principal means of orientation can easily be shown by the following experiment.

A bee is trained to a petri dish laid on blue paper and filled with syrup scented with orange scent; this bee is then marked (Experiments 84 and 101). Four other dishes are arranged at some distance away, two of which stand on blue paper and are not scented, whereas the other two are scented with orange oil and stand, one on yellow paper and the other on green. Increasing numbers of bees will soon be found on the orange-scented dishes, but a considerable time generally elapses before the unscented dishes are visited.

In an observation hive, which is a hive with a glass front, the nectar dance of the marked bee can be observed directly. But even without this it is still possible to observe the dance at the entrance to any hive, especially on a wet or chilly day when there is relatively little bee activity. If the hive from which the marked bee came is known, her return to it can be watched, and soon quite a crowd of bees will be seen leaving the hive and searching for the food supply. A rich harvest of pollen brought back to the hive also provokes great interest; the dance in this case is particularly conspicuous because the pollen finders carry the colored pollen in their "baskets." Originally von Frisch thought that nectar and pollen induce different types of dancing; but he now thinks that the differences are caused mainly by differences in the distance of the source of food. In addition, he has found the orientation of a forager's dance indicates the direction of the necessary flight.

CHAPTER VIII

Gravity

EXPERIMENT 59. Geotaxis of *Nepa* (2)

Animals and apparatus: A water bug of the genus *Nepa;* seesaw as described; aquarium.

Many insects are able to crawl upward on a vertical wall. They very clearly orient themselves away from the center of the earth. But, as far as we know, they have no special organs for the perception of gravity; and in this they differ from many crustaceans—which have statoliths —and all vertebrates—which perceive it by means of the labyrinth of the inner ear. The water bug *Nepa apiculata,* however, has on the ventral side of its abdomen eight structures, which are very peculiar static organs. These consist each of an air bubble in a hollow lined with tactile hairs; if the air is removed from these "statocysts," or if they are destroyed, the insect is no longer able to react to gravity. The intact *Nepa* can be used to demonstrate negative geotaxis—that is, movement away from the center of the earth—by the following method (Fig. 20). A seesaw is formed from a piece of wood 2 mm. thick and 30 cm. × 10 cm. in area, and a rod resting on the bottom of the aquarium (the rod should, of course, be sufficiently heavy to prevent its floating). The aquarium is filled with water deep enough to prevent any part of the board from coming out of the water; and a *Nepa* is then put on the part of the seesaw which is touching the bottom. The *Nepa* will soon start crawling up the inclined surface until it reaches a

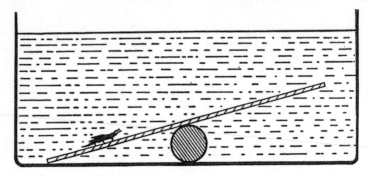

Fig. 20. The water bug *Nepa* on the submerged seesaw.

point where the equilibrium of the platform is disturbed and the seesaw tilts over. The insect may still go on for a little way in the same direction, but as a rule it will at once turn around and proceed upward until the board tilts again, and so on. Insects whose static organs have been destroyed do not show this reaction.

NOTE. If the seesaw is not well constructed, it will not tip under the weight of the insect alone; but the geotactic reaction will show when the position of the seesaw is changed by the experimenter. Care must be taken that illumination does not influence the reactions too strongly.

EXPERIMENT 60. Inversion of the Geotactic Reactions in Water Beetles (4)

Animals and apparatus: Aquarium with *Dytiscus;* cork; etherizer; acetone glue.

As already described in Experiment 16, many water beetles carry under their elytra a supply of air—which they normally bring into contact with the atmosphere from time to time by going to the surface of the water. In this way they effect an exchange of oxygen and carbon dioxide. After each "breath" the beetles swim downward again, hunting for their food; and they also go down when they are threatened in any way. Obviously the beetles know which is up and which is down. They are kept in their normal position in the water purely mechanically, by the air under their wings; this can be shown by etherizing a beetle and then submerging it in water, when it will be found to float on the surface with its back uppermost. Now, if a bit of cork is fixed to the ventral side of the abdomen of a dry beetle with an acetone glue, a very interesting change in behavior can be observed (provided that the bit of cork is sufficiently large to invert the insect's position in the water, but not large enough to make locomotion impossible). The insects will go to the bottom in search of air, and to the surface if they are threatened.

EXPERIMENT 61. Reversal of Geotaxis (62)

Animals and apparatus: Nymphs of *Diapheromera*, flies, ants, etc.; unsharpened pencil; glass tubing 2 feet long; cotton wool to stopper tubing.

Experiment 76 indicates that the young nymphs of *Diapheromera*, activated by negative geotaxis and led by the vertical contours, are directed up the stem of their food plant to the branches, and finally to the leaves on which they feed. If this behavior were so stereotyped that it could not be modified, one would expect to find all sorts of insects assembled at the tips of the branches desperately trying to get farther; but, in fact, such behavior is never found. A reversal of the reaction may occur in various ways. For instance, an insect may fall off and start again; or, if winged, it may take flight and move elsewhere. The latter type of behavior can be seen by letting a ladybird crawl up a finger held vertically, until it flies away. If a similar experiment is tried with a stick insect nymph, using a pencil for it to crawl up, one can generally observe that it will try for some time when it reaches the top to get a little higher; then all of a sudden it will turn through 180 degrees and start resolutely walking down again. If during this movement the pencil is turned upside down, the insect may turn on its own account so as to go on moving downward; and if it reaches the lower end of the pencil it may again reverse its direction. Clearly, when the first change in direction is made, the insect has changed its mood (or whatever one calls it), not because of a change in the external situation, but owing to its previous experience that there was no further way up. A similar reaction can be observed in a fly, a bee, or an ant—or in almost any insect—which is confined in a long container such as a closed glass tube.

CHAPTER IX

Temperature

EXPERIMENT 62. Perception of Texture, Temperature, and Smell by the Pig Louse, *Haematopinus suis* (93)

Animals and apparatus: Haematopinus suis (pig louse); glass plate; test tube of water at 40°C.

If a pig louse is taken off a pig and set upon a glass plate, it will keep on moving about; whereas if it is placed upon a piece of cloth (Experiment 48), it will stop moving. This difference in behavior can be attributed to the insect's perception of the different surface qualities.

The moving animal is attracted by warmth, a faculty which will clearly help it when it is searching for a host. This attraction can be shown by moving a test tube filled with water at a temperature of about 40°C. slowly in front of a louse when it is on the glass plate. The insect will follow it about. It will also follow the finger of the experimenter and will investigate it with its antennae; whereas it makes no attempt to investigate the test tube. This indicates that *Haematopinus* is attracted by the smell as well as by warmth.

EXPERIMENT 63. Temperature Preferences in Insects (79, 89, 92)

Animals and apparatus: Larval and adult houseflies; metal bar as described; large container; three stands; thermometer; small burner; ice in tin can.

Insects, like most other animals, show preferences for certain temperatures. The choice is dependent on internal conditions, e.g., age and also on such external factors as humidity. If insects of any species are given the choice between different temperatures, they will tend to collect at one of these, which is then called the preferred temperature. Thus, by choosing favorable conditions, insects can to some extent compensate for the lack of a constant blood temperature. The preferred temperature always lies between a low temperature at which motor activity just begins (the chill-coma temperature) and the thermal death point, at which the animal dies.

Different arrangements are needed for demonstrating the preferred temperatures in terrestrial and aquatic insects (the latter being more difficult subjects for experiment). An apparatus for testing the temperature preferences of terrestrial insects can be made as follows: A flat piece of copper or brass one inch thick, two inches wide, and fifteen inches or more long, is used as the bottom of a container which is made either of glass or of some transparent plastic; this container must be shorter than the metal base upon which it is to stand. The metal base is laid on two supports so that it overlaps them at both ends. On one end is placed a half-pound tin can containing some ice or cold water; and underneath the other end is arranged a small flame, which can be regulated. After ten minutes, a reasonable temperature gradient usually develops, and the container can be opened so that the bottom temperatures at various points can be measured. This can be done by setting the bulb of a laboratory thermometer on the metal, at points marked with pencil at every two inches along the bar and numbered; it is convenient to fix the thermometer in a stand so that it need not be held. After one series of measurements has been noted, a second series should be made, and there should not be any great difference between the recorded measurements in the two series.

For the experiment proper, a number of insects of one species is put in the container, on a strip of paper on the metal base. The distribution of the animals is observed after varying periods. Sometimes it is an advantage to use filter paper which is slightly moistened; but it is not possible in such an arrangement to keep a constant humidity throughout the container, as vapor will perpetually migrate from the hotter to the colder parts. The preferred temperature of the species used should lie somewhere in the middle of the gradient. The following figures for preferred temperatures may be useful in giving some idea of the range of temperatures needed. Young maggots of houseflies between 30° and 37°C.; full-grown larvae below 15°C.; the adult *Musca* about 33°; the biting *Stomoxys* 28°; and *Fannia* 24°. Cockroaches prefer medium temperatures, between 20° and 29°C., and various beetles show a wide range of choice; on the whole, it will be found that no region need be below 10°C. nor above 38°C.

It is interesting not only to observe the preferred region of the bulk of the insects but also to watch the movements of single individuals. The insect will usually move about rather restlessly at temperatures that are too high and less quickly at those that are too low for its taste, whereas it will keep fairly quiet in the preferred region. Occasionally one may observe changes in the direction of movement, when it leads away from the optimum. The results of subsequent experiments can be recorded on squared paper, on which the abscissae denote the temperatures of the various regions, and the ordinates, from above downward, the subsequent measurements. Times and temperatures can be entered on the table, and the numbers found at the various places recorded in the form of figures or of graphs.

EXPERIMENT 64. Temperature Preference of
Drosophila Larvae (89)

Animals and apparatus: Drosophila culture; agar-maize-
yeast food; large petri dish; tripod; asbestos mat; small
burner or electric lamp.

Most insects are oriented to a large extent by temperature, and if they are offered a choice will collect at the place
where the temperature is nearest to the one that they prefer. This can easily be shown in the larvae of many Diptera,
for example in *Drosophila,* where it will be found to lie
between 30° and 37°C. An easy way of demonstrating this
is to take a large petri dish, ten inches in diameter (or
any other large flat dish which can be completely covered),
and fill it to a depth of about a quarter of an inch with
the agar-maize-yeast mixture used for *Drosophila* culture
(p. 171). After cooling, the surface of the medium is
heavily painted with a thick emulsion of baker's yeast.
About a dozen adult *Drosophilae* are now shaken onto the
upturned lid of the dish, which is then put into position
over the bottom. The whole dish is then kept in a moist
and warm place until larvae are seen crawling about in
the agar. If the temperature is kept at about 28°C., third-
instar larvae will be found on the fourth day. The lid of the
dish should be lifted daily so that the air is thoroughly
renewed.

When the food is full of larvae, the dish is placed on a
tripod. A very small flame, or an electric-light bulb, is put
underneath it so that it warms only a part of the under
surface. One way of doing this is to put under the dish
an asbestos mat in which a circle has been cut, about three
centimeters in diameter, so that the hole in the asbestos
comes just above the source of heat. After some time it will

be seen that the larvae will begin to migrate in all directions away from the hot spot: if the heat is intense, they will try to escape onto the lid; but if the heat is only moderate, and the experiment is conducted in a cool room, they may collect in a ring around the heated region, especially if the heating is interrupted from time to time. Another way of showing the reaction is to take a culture bottle containing adult larvae and immerse it up to the level of the medium in hot water at from 70° to 80°C. The larvae will then be found on the surface with their heads turned toward the center (Fig. 21).

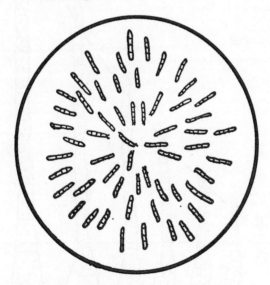

Fig. 21. Larvae of *Drosophila* on the surface of food in a bottle. They are shown crawling toward the center, as a result of heat coming from below and outside.

EXPERIMENT 65. Perception of Radiant Heat in the Stick Insect *Diapheromera femorata* (19)

Animals and apparatus: Stick insects; metal knitting needle; cork; magnifying glass.

An adult stick insect is rolled on the table with two fingers until it becomes cataleptic (Experiment 43). It is then arranged on a raised object, such as a block of wood or a book, so that the antennae and the front legs—when

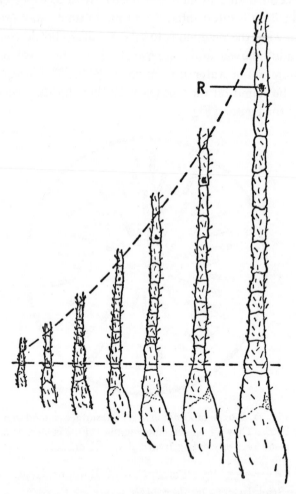

Fig. 22. Growth of the left antenna of a stick insect. Consecutive instars show the apparent movement of the heat receptor, R, owing to subdivision of segments. (After Cappe de Baillon)

stretched forward—project over the edge. The legs can be gently separated from the antennae until there is some distance between them. A metal knitting needle held in a cork is heated in a flame until it is hot, but not red-hot. It is then held horizontally at right angles to the antennae, and about half an inch away from their tips, and is slowly moved nearer to the animal, either above or below the antennae. Great care must be taken not to overheat the contents of the antennae. When the heat receptor is reached (about a third of the length away from the base of the antenna), the antennae are suddenly jerked back, and the whole animal becomes lively and starts walking away.

The heat is perceived by a curious flat organ rather like a poached egg, which can just be seen with a magnifying glass. Locate this on the dorsal surface at the segment which was sensitive to the hot knitting needle. If the reaction is not observed when a temperature of about 70°C. is used, it will probably be found that the organ lies in a more proximal segment (always in nymphs, see Fig. 22). It may vary in position in other species of stick insects.

An alternative method of applying the heat is to concentrate an image of the sun on the antenna with a magnifying glass and slowly move it toward the animal.

It should be pointed out that the described reaction to radiant heat is not necessarily the normal response of the antennal organ.

CHAPTER X

Reactions to Light

EXPERIMENT 66. Painting the Eyes of Insects (12)

Animals and apparatus: Black paint; brush; etherizer; six insects of the same species.

In human beings, the sense organs not only initiate motor reactions but also influence posture and the tension of the muscles when resting. In man and in other vertebrates, most of this is effected through the semicircular canals and ampullae in the ear. In insects, however, which have no such perception of rotation or gravity, the eyes are much more important. Consequently, it is possible to induce various anomalous postures and movements in many species of insects by covering one eye, or parts of one or both eyes, with black paint. This paint can be prepared either by mixing black water color with gum arabic or by using a quickly evaporating acetone paint. Especially suitable insects for such an experiment are certain of the predatory flies, such as those which are found abundantly on sheep dung. But to a lesser degree, almost any insect is suitable. To get a good impression of the results, it is necessary to compare variously treated individuals with each other and with untreated animals. At least half a dozen individuals of a species are therefore needed. In one, the eyes should be untouched; in another the right and in another the left eye should be painted; and in the others either the upper or the lower parts of both eyes, or both left or both right halves. The paint should be applied while the insects are etherized; and after they have recovered, their attitudes should be watched, preferably at various illuminations, e.g., in diffused daylight and in a dark room variously lighted. In certain conditions, not only very striking abnormal postures can be observed but also movement in circles and other conspicuously disturbed behavior. The reactions are not always very regular, and further changes in behavior may be observed when the animal is beginning to get used to the new condition.

EXPERIMENT 67. Phototonus and Flying Reflex (56)

Animals and apparatus: Hawk moth; lightproof box about 3 inches cube; dark room; orange or yellow light.

It is well known that insects have different periods of activity; some are nocturnal, some diurnal, and others fly by twilight. The factors controlling insect activities are partly internal and partly environmental; among the latter, temperature and light are probably the most important. The influence of light can easily be demonstrated in the various hawk moths, most of which are active in the twilight. If the hawk moth, whose pupae can be obtained cheaply, is put into a dark box measuring about three inches each way, it will remain there motionless for a day or longer. If the box is opened in the evening, in a dark or an almost dark room, the moth will still not begin to move. But the moment that the beam of a yellow light such as is used in a photographic darkroom, or the light from a distant lamp, reaches the eyes of the moth, it will stretch its forelegs and start humming and vibrating its wings. This vibrating may be compared with warming the engines of an airplane before the start of a flight. After a time, depending on the room temperature, the moth will take off and either hover or fly about, bumping into the walls of the room. If the light is turned off during the flight, the moth immediately stops flying and falls to the ground, where it can be found later. Cessation of flight when a light is turned off can also be heard on summer evenings, when flies stop buzzing and may even fall to the ground.

EXPERIMENT 68. The Shadow Reflex in Mosquito Larvae

Animals and apparatus: Mosquito larvae and pupae; glass jar.

Mosquito larvae are often found in stagnant water, e.g., in rain-water butts, where they usually hang with the head downward and with the posterior spiracles at the surface of the water. The pupae are also found near the surface; but they have their earlike anterior spiracles upward. If the sun is shining on the water, it is easy to make both the larvae and the pupae dive by moving the shadow of one's hand across the surface of the water, though they will return to the surface after a matter of seconds. A similar shadow reflex is found in many other animals, e.g., in barnacles and some of the marine mollusks. It is believed that it serves to preserve the animals that show the reflex from swiftly moving predators. There is no definite relation between the direction in which the shadow moves and the direction of flight; it is merely the reduction of the light intensity which causes a downward movement. The decrease in the light intensity must assume certain proportions to be effective, and its effectiveness varies according to the intensity of the initial illumination. By experimenting over a wide range of light intensities, one gets a correspondingly wide range of shadow thresholds.

A rough demonstration of this reaction can be made in the following way: A few mosquito larvae and pupae are put into a glass jar holding about a quart of water, and the jar is put on a sunny window sill so that the sun shines full upon it. When the insects have settled near the surface of the water, the hand is moved across the window so that its shadow travels across the surface and falls upon the larvae and pupae. These will immediately dive. If, however, the jar is placed so that it is not directly illuminated by the sun, the movement of the hand will not induce any reaction. Apparently the decrease in illumination under these circumstances is not big enough or sudden enough to be effective.

Another phenomenon which can be studied at the same time is habituation, which may be a sort of fatigue. After the experiment in sunlight has been repeated several times, most of the larvae and pupae will fail to react; but when they have had a rest of about twenty minutes they will dive again.

EXPERIMENT 69. Chasing Flies Out of the Window (12)

Animals and apparatus: Houseflies, blowflies; stiff paper or cardboard.

The old theory of tropisms assumed that there was always a direct relationship between the direction of a stimulus and the individual's response to it. In addition, it was assumed that the organism in reacting would bend or move into a more favorable situation. For instance, green motile algae would always move toward the source of light and thus be better able to assimilate. It was soon found that the relationship was rarely as simple as this, and in particular there need not always be a definite relation between the direction of the stimulus and the direction of the movement. This can easily be shown by chasing flies out of a window or onto the windowpanes. Flies of various species can be used; but the blowfly *Calliphora vomitoria* gives particularly good results. By violently and quite indiscriminately flapping at the flies in a room with a piece of cardboard or stiff paper, they will be made to head straight for the window (see Experiment 47). Here they will either get out or hit against the glass—although previously they had paid no attention to the outside world. Now, it is possible to describe this behavior in two ways. Either it may be said that the irritated flies become positively phototactic, and in this condition fly toward the light. Or alternatively one may say that, although the stimulus actually setting the flies to flight (i.e., the flapping) occurs in all sorts of directions, the flies' reaction is directed definitely in relation to the light, even if by itself it would not cause the flies to move. The first description would still be in keeping with the early concept of phototropism; but whichever explanation is preferred, the end achieved is clear—namely, that the reaction enables the flies to escape from a disturbed and potentially dangerous room into safety.

If a fly is chased repeatedly against a closed window, it will change its behavior and either take off in a different direction or cease altogether to fly away.

EXPERIMENT 70. Various Forms of Phototaxis (39)

Animals and apparatus: Flies, bees, beetles, silver fish, flour moth larvae; black paint; lamp; etherizer.

In certain situations, it seems natural to human beings to go toward a light. If a man has lost his way in the fields at night, or in a boat at sea, a light is immediately attractive. If such a person were asked how he managed to approach the light, the answer would be that he fixed it in the middle of the visual field and then went toward it in as straight a line as possible. Under other conditions, a light may have exactly the opposite effect. For instance, people being pursued will try to get away from it. To the unsophisticated mind, it would seem natural for animals to behave in the same way and go either toward or away from a light. This is the case in many insects (e.g., in Diptera, Hymenoptera, and beetles), but as we do not know much about their consciousness, we call their reactions positive or negative phototaxis.

It would not be difficult for a man with only one eye to approach such a target as a light directly; and the insects which have just been mentioned can also do it when one of the eyes has been blackened (Experiment 66). But many insects show a rather different type of behavior after one eye has been blackened—at least for some time, which suggests that a different mechanism of orientation is involved. Silver fish (*Lepisma saccharina*), the larvae of flour moths (*Ephestia*), and bloodworms (larvae of *Chironomus*) all show this second type of behavior. Typically, such insects when they are blinded in one eye do not move in a straight line toward a light, but progress in irregular circles or spirals.

This behavior cannot be explained on the assumption that the insects fix the light with their eyes. It must rather be assumed that the right and left eyes have a certain antagonistic effect, which results in a straight line being followed only when light perception on both sides is equal. Thus, approach to light may be effected by quite different mechanisms.

EXPERIMENT 71. Negative   Phototaxis   of
the Book Louse *Atropos pulsatoria*

Animals and apparatus: Decaying matter containing
book lice or blowfly maggots; darkened room and two table
lamps; smooth brown paper.

In old books, especially if they have been kept in a damp
place, large numbers of pale, wingless insects about one to
two millimeters long may be found. These are called book
lice. These and other similar species are also found in drying vegetable matter, in insect collections, in *Drosophila*
food which has been left for several weeks in a flat dish,
and in greenhouses and garden sheds. It is usually impossible to detect their presence by mere inspection, because
they hide; but by shaking the material over a table, dozens
and even hundreds can often be discovered. If a desk lamp
is arranged so that its light shines on the scattered book
lice on one side of the table, and all other lights are turned
off, the insects will march directly away from the source
of light. If the position of the lamp is changed, the insects,
too, will change their direction. Interesting observations
can be made by putting two lamps on the table at various
angles and distances from the insects. The routes of individual insects can be cautiously drawn with a pencil if
the lice are allowed to crawl on smooth brown paper instead of on the table (white paper is not so good for this
purpose). If a bit of the material from which the insects
originally came is put on the table, a certain number of
them will seek its shelter, attracted by the shadow and also
probably to some extent by the humidity. Similar phenomena can be observed in blowfly maggots under suitable
conditions.

EXPERIMENT 72. Light Compass Reaction
(7)

Animals and apparatus: Ants following a track; two tumblers.

Insects such as the social ants, bees, and termites, which make regular excursions from their nests, must find their way home or to a source of food by various means—such as by recognizing conspicuous landmarks or by a sense of distances and directions. In monotonous territory, the direction of the sun can also be used as a means of orientation. This may be very simply demonstrated if a path or closely cut lawn can be found fully exposed to the sun and frequented by ants. If in such territory ants are observed following any definite directions on a bright day, the following experiment can be carried out. The directions in which the ants are moving should be noted as accurately as possible, and a tumbler is then put over one or more of the outgoing ants and another over some of the ants that are returning. (Care must be taken to make sure that the ants cannot escape.) After two hours the tumblers are lifted and the directions which the ants then follow are observed. If the conditions have been favorable, it will be found that they will deviate from their original directions by about 30°, corresponding to the progress of the sun during the two hours.

EXPERIMENT 73. Change of Direction in an Insect's Movements When the Direction of the Light Is Changed (12)

Animals and apparatus: Ladybirds or earwigs, stick insects; two electric lights; insulated wire and insulating tape; double and single switches.

The following arrangement is useful for many experiments on the light orientation of insects. Two electric bulbs, A and B, are connected by insulated wire, in such a way that they can be lighted one at a time, or one can be switched on and off while the other is alight. This is most simply done by means of a double switch or three switches as indicated in Fig. 23. If the switch, D, is operated, both

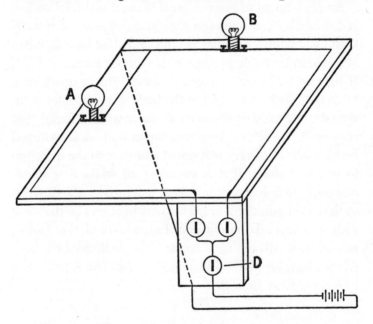

Fig. 23. Arrangement of light bulbs and switches, enabling the experimenter to use illumination from one or both of two sources.

bulbs may be alight simultaneously or alternately; and when the double switch lights them at the same time, the single switch can be used to switch bulb B on and off. By varying the position and the candle power of the two bulbs, many of the situations used for testing phototactic behavior can be produced. For instance, this method can be used to see whether an insect will crawl toward one of two simultaneously shining lights of equal intensity and distance; or whether it will crawl somewhere in between them. It may also show whether an insect is attracted by the lesser or the stronger of two lights. Further, one can discover whether switching on a second light changes the orientation toward the first light.

An experiment of more general interest is the following. It has often been observed that many species of insects, such as ladybirds or other beetles and stick insects, move at a particular angle in respect to a strong source of light. If the two bulbs are arranged at some distance apart, on a table in a dark room, and individuals of the species mentioned are placed in between them, it will be found that they walk in various directions when bulb A is switched on by itself. But every individual will stick to the direction in which it starts. If A is switched off while B is simultaneously switched on, the animal will turn by 180 degrees, so that its orientation toward the new light will be the same as it was toward the old one. Individuals of the species named will always turn toward the extinguished light when changing their direction, but *Lithobius* will, as a rule, turn away from it.

EXPERIMENT 74. Light Compass Reaction in Caterpillars, Beetles, and Stick Insects (11, 14, 47)

Animals and apparatus: Cabbage white caterpillars; beetles or stick insects; turntable (Exp. 78); dark room; table lamp.

Caterpillars of the cabbage white butterfly, or of butterflies of the genus *Vanessa*, can walk on a line making a constant angle with the sun's rays in the same way as the ants described in Experiment 72. If they are allowed to walk on a turntable (like the one used in Experiment 78) in bright sunlight, they will turn and go on walking in exactly the same direction as before when the upper plate has been turned through an angle of 90 degrees. Clearly, the sun is one of their means of orientation.

A similar reaction can be observed in beetles such as ladybirds, in earwigs, and in stick insects. Beetles (suitably shielded from direct sunlight) can be made to walk in a circle by reflecting the sun's rays onto them with a mirror.

The same effect can be produced in a dark room by letting the insects walk on a table while a single light is burning. If this light is moved, or if it is turned out while another is turned on, the insects will turn in such a way that the path followed still makes the same angle with the line joining the insect's body to the source of light as it did before. It should be noted that the insects do not move directly toward or away from the light but may move at almost any angle to it.

EXPERIMENT 75. Dorsal Light Reflex in Aquatic Insects (12)

Animals and apparatus: Glass vessel; two electric-light bulbs; double and single switches; May fly larvae, *Dytiscus,* or *Notonecta.*

It has been stated that most insects have one or more natural postures, usually with the ventral side downward or toward the substratum. In many cases this position is achieved by the perception of contact stimuli; but in others it is caused by light orientation. Good examples of this latter type of behavior are seen in some larvae of ephemerids (May flies), and among water beetles such as *Dytiscus,* and in the water boatmen, or *Notonecta* (Fig. 24).

A demonstration can easily be given by using the double light described in Experiment 73 to illuminate a small glass aquarium or a large jam jar. The vessel should be filled with water and placed on a stand so that one bulb can be ar-

Fig. 24. The water boatman *Notonecta undulata*.

ranged just underneath the glass bottom of the container and the other above the water surface. When the whole arrangement is set up in a fairly dark room, individuals of suitable insects will turn their backs toward the light regardless of whether it comes from above or below; and when the illumination is changed, they will also change their orientation.

A similar type of behavior is found in some flying insects, e.g., in dragonflies; but the necessity for a flying insect to maintain its position against the force of gravity makes a demonstration much more difficult in this case.

EXPERIMENT 76. Photohorotaxis in the Nymphs of Stick Insects (51, 61, 90)

Animals and apparatus: Newly hatched nymphs of stick insects; stiff white paper or thin card; paper clips; dark paper.

Most leaf-eating insects, and those whose larvae eat leaves, deposit their eggs on the plants on which they feed, so that the young have no great difficulty in getting to their food. Some insects, however, and, in particular, stick insects, drop their hard-shelled eggs, so that they fall to the ground. The young larvae ("nymphs") emerging from these eggs must therefore find their way up the bushes and trees on whose leaves they will feed. One of the things which makes it possible for them to do this is the attraction that vertical contours have for them, especially dark contours against a lighter background.

This attraction can be demonstrated in the following way: A white sheet of stiff paper or thin card, at least two yards long and half a yard wide, is made into a hollow cylinder half a yard high; and the ends are fixed in position with paper clips. Strips of dark paper of various widths, and rather longer than the height of the cylinder, are cut, and the ends are bent so that the strips can hang on the cylinder's rim closely applied to its inner wall. The whole arrangement is put on a table underneath a light, which should be in a line with the center of the cylinder. In a first experiment three black strips about two inches wide may be used hung at approximately equal distances apart.

Some newly hatched nymphs, which may still be dragging their eggshells, are put on the table in the middle of the cylinder. After a few minutes most of them will be found moving toward one of the black strips, and some will begin to crawl up the wall. If much wider black strips are used, for instance two, each of which covers a quarter of the wall, the nymphs can be seen to aim at the vertical border between dark and light, the simplest contour imaginable. (Fig. 25.) This reaction cannot therefore be described as either positive or negative phototaxis, and is named photohorotaxis (from the Greek word *horos*, "a border"; the same root occurs in the word "horizon").

By using cylinders and strips of various colors and shades, information can be gleaned about the color perception of the nymphs. And their visual acuity can be estimated by using very narrow strips. This roughly agrees with the angular distance of the facets in the eyes. A further experiment can be made using strips that are not vertical.

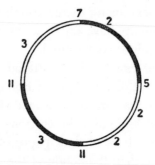

Fig. 25. Section through a hollow cylinder made from white cardboard with black strips. The numbers show the distribution of first-instar larvae of *Diapheromera* crawling up the cylinder after being released from the center of its base. The majority clearly move toward the vertical edges between black and white.

The reaction described is closely related to some of the optomotor reactions described in Experiment 78. It may also be observed in various caterpillars. Houseflies, too, can often be seen to run along dark contours, such as the shadow cast onto the ceiling by the wire of a pendant lamp.

EXPERIMENT 77. Optomotor Reactions in Mosquitoes (71)

Animals and apparatus: Mosquitoes; two dinner plates; stiff paper or card cylinder painted inside with vertical stripes.

Mosquitoes can hover in approximately one spot like a helicopter, and they are suitable for a demonstration of optomotor reactions during flight. By using the apparatus described in Experiment 78, any mosquito can be induced to turn around following the stripes on a revolving cylinder. The mosquito is put into a glass vial, one inch in diameter and four inches long, which is set in the middle of the turning cylinder. By shaking the vial, the mosquito can be made to fly, and it will then follow the direction of the rotating stripes. The small number of facets in a mosquito's eye results in a low visual acuity, as compared, for instance, with a fly. Thus the best reaction will be obtained by using five black and five white stripes of equal width.

Mosquitoes are sometimes observed flying against a slight wind; but in stormy weather they do not fly at all, and it used to be assumed that they were oriented by the air current. It seems, however, very likely that they are oriented by the apparent movement of the solid objects over which the wind carries them, for which they compensate by an optomotor reaction similar to the one just described.

EXPERIMENT 78. Optomotor Reaction (46)

Animals and apparatus: Ants, flies, stick insects, bees; two dinner plates; stiff paper or card cylinder painted inside with vertical stripes; petri dish or tumbler; ruby light.

If a human being is turned on a turntable, the movement is apparent not only to the eyes but also to the semicircular canal system and to the mechanical sense organs; so that even if the eyes are closed, it is still possible to feel in which direction the table is being turned. Insects do not possess a sense organ for the reception of rotational acceleration, but many of them react very accurately to visual movement.

The simplest way of demonstrating this is to enclose a suitable insect in a glass vessel and to move a cylinder marked with vertical stripes around it. But it makes no difference to the insect's reaction if it and the container together are moved against a stationary background of stripes. A simple way of doing this is to take two plates equal in size (and preferably without much decoration) and to lay one on the other with water in between them, so that the upper one rotates easily on the lower. The two plates are put underneath a light, and a cylinder is put around them similar to the one used in Experiment 76, but smaller and with perhaps twelve white and twelve black stripes. (Fig. 26.) An ant or a young stick insect is put in

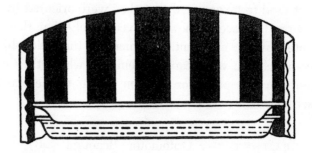

Fig. 26. Floating turntable and striped cylinder for the study of optomotor reactions.

the center of the top plate, which is rotated gently. The insect will soon be seen to turn its head and antennae against the direction in which it is being rotated; and it will even walk in circles, or parts of circles, always in the direction in which the stationary pattern appears to move.

If flying insects are used for the experiment, a petri dish or a tumbler can be put over them. It will be observed that the insects will circle only when they are on the floor

or the ceiling of their container. When they are sitting or
crawling on the vertical walls, they will not be deflected
but will only show peculiar postures. They may, for example, put the head on one side, nearer to or further from
the glass, as if in an attempt to follow the apparent rotation as far as possible. If one takes the trouble to make the
cylinder rotate by suspending it by a string, the same reactions can be observed in the insects on the stationary
plate. The rate of turning should be fairly slow, about once
in one or two seconds, and the results will be especially
clear if the direction is reversed.

By using stripes of various widths, shades, and colors
and by varying the illumination, one can investigate visual
acuity, discrimination for brightness, and color sense. In
many insects, no turning reactions will be observed if a
ruby light is used for illuminating, which presumably
means that with this light the light stripes are indistinguish-
able from the black. In other words, the visible spectrum
for insects is shorter at the red end than it is for humans.
A reaction would, however, often be observed if some ultra-
violet light were added to the red light, since this light
can be perceived by insects although it is invisible to human eyes.

EXPERIMENT 79. Catching of a Ball by a
Hover Fly (12)

Animals and apparatus: Hover flies; glass jar of 2-quart
capacity or larger; cotton wool; black thread; muslin.

Fairly large flies of a greenish-yellow color can often be
found on sheep dung. They are flies of a predacious type
belonging to the family of Syrphidae, and they are readily
attracted by small moving objects. If a small ball of cotton
wool is rolled in the hand to about the size of a pea and

is then fastened on to the end of a piece of black thread, it can be used to show this attraction. One of the flies is caught and put into a large glass jar with a muslin cover. Through the cover the black thread passes so that the ball of cotton wool hangs freely in the jar. If the ball is dangled about in front of the fly, it will very often attack it and grasp it with all six legs, holding on to it for a considerable time. The fly can be induced to repeat the action several times.

If a dark-colored ball is used, a similar experiment can be made on male houseflies, which will often be found to pursue the ball, mistaking it for a female and attempting to mate with it. (Experiment 81.)

EXPERIMENT 80. Attraction of Male House-flies, *Musca domestica,* to Bits of Wool (53)

Animals and apparatus: Male houseflies; insect cage about one foot in each direction; gray cardboard; thick wool, white, black, and shades of gray.

Many housewives have been disgusted by pairing house-flies falling into their pots and pans. The mating reaction of the male housefly is certainly a very common and conspicuous event. It is peculiar, moreover, because it does not appear to depend very much on the movement of the object of the male's attentions, but simply on size and darkness of color. Certain orchids have made use of a similar reaction in some of the male flies by which they are pollinated. The flowers imitate female flies in their shape and color, so that the male flies trying to mate merely succeed in pollinating the orchids.

In houseflies the reaction can be demonstrated in the following way. Two dozen male houseflies, which can be distinguished from the females by their larger eyes and by the shape of the abdomen (Fig. 27), are either caught by hand (Experiment 47), trapped, or bred and are then kept apart from females for two days and fed on a bit of fish.

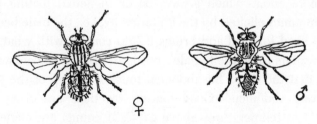

Fig. 27. Female and male houseflies.

A cage is needed, which is about a foot each way, with a cardboard bottom, but with walls made either of muslin or of transparent plastic material. Ordinary insect cages can, of course, be used. One side of the cage is used as a door, and the opposite side is fully covered with a sheet of gray cardboard, on which there are knots of thick wool ranging from white to black through various shades of gray. There should be about thirty of these twisted into little lumps of the approximate size of a female housefly, the distance between them being about an inch and a half. The gray cardboard is fixed to the back wall of the cage so that the lumps of wool are vertical, and the cage is opened with the door directed away from the source of light. The sex-starved male flies are then released in the cage and the door is closed. The cage is turned so that light falls on the wool, and the behavior of the flies is observed.

Two chains of reactions can usually be seen. In the first place, the flies can be observed walking from one piece of wool to another, and occasionally making contact with one of them. Secondly, more definite mating reactions may occur. These will usually be of the following kind: The male settles down on the card at a short distance from a piece of wool, and then stalks slowly toward it and halts at about a centimeter away from it; then he suddenly leaps onto it and makes a strong buzzing noise with his wings. Further, the reactions which always occur in actual mating are sometimes elicited by the imitation fly, i.e., the male bends his head forward and brings it into contact with what he considers to be the female's head, and then tilts backward so that the tip of his abdomen touches the tip of the "female's abdomen." Good mating reactions are observed only at temperatures above 21°C. If counts are made of the number of visits paid by one fly to the various stitches, it will be found that position has some influence. But the main result will be that the darker wools are more frequently mistaken for females than the lighter ones, while the white pieces are hardly visited at all.

In very dim light the males do not discriminate between lighter and darker lumps; but in a wide range of brighter lights they can do so, although in full sunlight the reaction becomes rather poor.

Variously colored wools can be used in this experiment, but it is much more difficult to interpret the results obtained. On the whole, it is the brightness of the colors that is perceived. The size and shape of the decoys also influence the reaction, and these can be made the subjects of other studies, especially when combined with alterations in the illumination.

The best technique to use in recording the tracks and reactions of the rapidly moving males is to have a full-scale drawing of the card with its lumps of wool, and to draw the movements in with pencil, having a special sign for the actual mounting. If the same experiment is carried out using female flies, the reactions are much less clear. The same thing applies in the case of males which have recently had opportunities for mating or which are less than three days old.

EXPERIMENT 81. Capture of Males of the
Lesser Housefly, *Fannia canicularis*, with a Black
Ball (12)

Apparatus: Black bead; black thread attached to stick; glue.

The lesser housefly reacts most strongly to moving objects, and a striking experiment can be performed by using a small black ball to catch the male flies. A small black bead about the size of a housefly is a suitable object to use for this purpose, strung on a piece of black thread which is fastened to a stick like a miniature fishing rod. If this is carried through the air in a room where there are houseflies, at a speed of two or three feet per second, some of the males will rush at the bead and try to settle upon it. If the bead has been dipped in glue, one or two of the flies will be caught on it, making the demonstration still more convincing.

EXPERIMENT 82. The Blue Preference of a
Hover Fly, *Bombylius major*, or other bombylid
flies (72)

Animals and apparatus: Bombylius major or other bombylid flies; blue flowers; cardboard; gray and blue paper in different shades.

Flowers are pollinated not only by bees and other Hymenoptera, and by beetles and midges, but also in some cases by flies. As shown in Experiment 84, bees can be trained to any color which they can recognize, although they may have some natural preferences. But many of the Diptera are difficult to train, and therefore they display very clearly any natural preferences that they may have. This can be shown in the following field experiment. On sunny days the hover fly *B. major* can often be observed visiting blue flowers. A piece of cardboard eight inches square is divided into sixteen squares; fourteen of these are covered with gray paper of various shades as indicated in Fig. 28, and of the remaining two, one is a dark blue

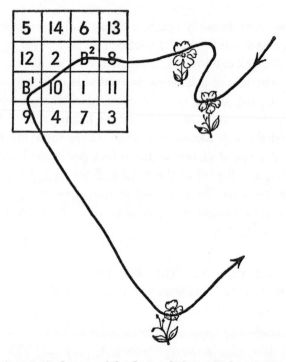

Fig. 28. Deflection of the fly *Bombylius,* which is visiting blue flowers, to two blue squares in a checkerboard. The other squares are made up of gray papers of various shades. (After Knoll)

and the other a light blue. The board is placed near blue flowers so that the sun falls on it, and the observer steps back a few paces and watches. If enough flies are present, it will be observed that they visit the blue squares just as they visit the blue flowers; in fact, they can often be seen to alternate between flowers and checkerboard, as shown in Fig. 28.

EXPERIMENT 83. Simultaneous Contrast in the Hummingbird Hawk Moth, *Macroglossum stellatarum* (72)

Animals and apparatus: Hummingbird hawk moth; gray paper; white, gray, and black cards.

The human eye is not able to measure absolute brightness. The main reason for this is its enormous capacity for adaptation—which is due to some extent to the widening and narrowing of the pupil, but to a still greater extent to chemical changes in the retina. Thus, the dark letters on the page of a book actually reflect more light when the book is read in the sunshine than the white page will do after sunset. Nevertheless, we always call the letters black and the page white. Clearly then, the terms light and dark are only relative, denoting the relative illumination of an object and its environment. A demonstration of this—called the simultaneous contrast—is as follows: Three circles one inch in diameter are cut from dark-gray paper. One is glued in the center of a white card four inches square, the second on a light-gray card, and the third on a black card. To the casual onlooker, the three circles will appear of quite different shades when viewed side by side, although they must be of the same objective brightness. The question is, do insects also perceive light and darkness in the same way that man does—that is to say, relatively? If the three cards are stuck to a plain wall facing a window early in the evening, particularly in autumn, the simultaneous contrast can be demonstrated by releasing in the room a hummingbird hawk moth. This day-flying moth looks for holes and crevices to hide in, and it will soon be found searching in the neighborhood of the gray on white; it may occasionally visit the gray on gray, but never the gray on black.

EXPERIMENT 84. Training a Group of Bees (71)

Animals and apparatus: Blue paper; petri dish; knitting needle (nonmetal); honey and sugar solutions.

Many interesting experiments can be carried out by training bees. The most difficult part of the training is to make the first bee come to an artificial source of food; but it can be done in the following way. On a bright day, when bees are out foraging, a piece of blue paper about a foot square or larger is smeared with honey and then displayed near the site where the training is to take place. The paper should be inspected at hourly intervals until some bees are found sitting on it and licking the honey. When this has happened, the blue paper can be removed. It is replaced by another piece which has not been smeared with honey, but on which a petri dish is placed containing a mixture of equal parts of honey and water. After some bees have become used to this food, further changes in the composition of the food can gradually be introduced. For instance, the honey can be replaced by sugar solution. Changes can also be made in the construction and position of the feeding vessel.

Sometimes the blue-paper method does not work and a more laborious method is required. For this the tip of a knitting needle (not made of metal) is dipped into a solution of equal parts of honey and water, so that a small drop clings to the tip but otherwise the needle remains clean.

Flowers, or preferably flowering shrubs, on which bees are collecting are approached with this implement, and the drop on its tip is brought near to a bee's proboscis when she is either sitting on a flower or is trying to get into one. When the bee begins to lick the honey, the needle is slowly withdrawn so that she follows it, and an attempt is made to induce her to sit on the needle while sucking the honey. When this happens, the needle is put down gently on the experimental table or elsewhere and left alone. The experimenter then takes one or two steps back and watches the bee. The attempt is successful if the bee, before flying away, is observed to circle around the needle or possibly even to settle down again. In this case, she will come back after a few minutes; and other bees from the same hive, which have been interested by the first bee's typical dancing movements, may soon follow. Once a few bees have become accustomed to the feeding place, they show great constancy to it; and if enough honey solution is supplied, the difficulty will not be that too few bees come, but that there are too many. This can, however, be checked by various means. The solution can be made more dilute; or it can be made more difficult of access by filling the petri dish with clean sand soaked with the syrup. It is a very pretty sight to see bees angrily digging in the dry sand once they have licked away all the syrup. If bees from two hives are trained to come to such a dish (e.g., black Caucasians and light Italians, which are easily distinguishable), fighting will ensue between the two different stocks—which try to carry one another away. This battle probably corresponds to the robbing of one hive by bees from another, which is so much dreaded by beekeepers. Occasionally wasps will also visit the feeding places, but they never come so regularly.

EXPERIMENT 85. The Sense of Form in Bees
(12)

Animals and apparatus: Bees; patterns on cardboard approximately four inches square; training table.

Many vertebrates seem to perceive shapes as human beings do, although usually with less accuracy. Birds can probably distinguish objects better than humans can. Insects, however, seem to perceive quite different qualities in visual patterns. The main features appreciated by a bee's form sense are the complexity of the pattern, i.e., the amount of contours and the differences in shade. It is not possible to train bees to visit triangles, squares, circles, ellipses, or crosses with four and three arms, in such a way that the bees do not confuse them; for these figures have approximately the same amount of circumference. However, patterns like the ones in Fig. 29 can easily be dis-

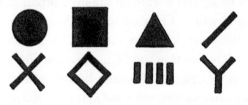

Fig. 29. Bees can distinguish the figures in the upper row from those in the lower; but they cannot discriminate between those in the upper row or those in the lower row. (After Hertz)

tinguished by the bee; although other patterns, which to the human eye have no obvious similarities, may be confused.

Two methods may be used for training. Beekeepers may either fix the pattern vertically in front of the entrances of the hives; or a horizontal arrangement can be used, such as the training table described in Experiment 84. In both cases, pairs of contrasting patterns are used, and food is offered with one but not with the other. After an hour's training no food is offered with either pattern, but the number of bees visiting both patterns are counted. Highly significant differences should be found after a few minutes.

EXPERIMENT 86. The Light Compass Reaction and a Light at Finite Distance (9)

Animals and apparatus: Earwig or stick insect; candle or small electric light; sheet of gray or brown paper one yard square; dark room.

In Experiment 72 it was shown that ants can orient their movements by the sun. But at night many insects also orient themselves by nearer lights. If an insect is moving away at an angle from a lamp, its path will not visibly diverge from a straight line. If, on the other hand, the insect is getting nearer to the lamp, it will be seen to approach the light on a curved line—actually a logarithmic spiral ending of necessity in the light itself. This is the reaction shown by the moth seeking the flame, which can be observed at any light in the open air in summer (Fig. 30). Thus this proverbial behavior is yet another mechanism leading animals toward a light. This reaction works satisfactorily in nature when the source of light, either the sun or the moon, is at such a distance that the rays reaching the insect are parallel. It leads, however, to disaster in the case of an artificial light at a relatively short distance. As a matter of fact, movement directly toward the sun or the moon (i.e., positive phototaxis) would be quite useless to the insect.

For a demonstration of the spiral track, a table should be covered with a large sheet of gray or brown paper, with a

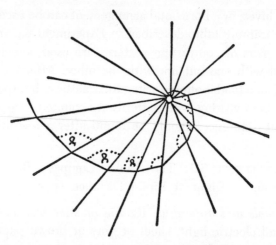

Fig. 30. The path of a moth flying into a light in a spiral track—owing to its maintaining a constant angle to the light. (After Buddenbrock)

candle or small electric light arranged in the middle of it. An earwig or a stick insect is then placed in a far corner of the paper facing the light. In many cases the insect will start moving somewhat askew toward the light, and its track can be traced with a pencil. After the insect has arrived in the neighborhood of the light, the light is removed. Lines can then be drawn radiating from the place where it was, and it will be found that the angles between these radii and the penciled track will have remained approximately the same throughout the whole of the insect's progress.

EXPERIMENT 87. Time of Emergence from the Pupae in *Drosophila melanogaster* (59, 64, 65)

Animals and apparatus: Drosophila culture bottles containing larvae and pupae; light-tight boxes.

Culture bottles of *Drosophila melanogaster* can be used

for a demonstration of the dependence of pupal emergence on the time of day. If the numbers of emerged flies are counted at two- or three-hour intervals, it will be found that the greatest numbers are recorded just before and during the early hours of illumination, while very few flies come out during the rest of the light period or in the earlier hours of darkness. Although each fly can emerge only once, the diurnal rhythm goes on in the population for two or three days if the cultures are kept in continual darkness. This indicates that an impression is left on the older larvae and pupae which is having a rhythmic effect on emergence. It is most likely that there is an organ responsible for this somewhere in the neighborhood of the eyes.

More elaborate methods must be used if the factors causing this periodicity are to be analyzed. To show that light is the main factor, two groups of bottles may be illuminated alternately or at various times. For this purpose, either two darkened rooms can be used in which electric light can be turned on during certain hours or the bottles can be enclosed for certain periods in light-tight boxes and can be kept in the light for the rest of the time. The boxes should not be airtight. During the peak hours of emergence, flies should be released and counted every hour, but this is not necessary at other times, when four- or five-hour intervals should be sufficient.

The results can best be presented in the form of a histogram on squared paper. In Fig. 31 the results obtained from four cultures are shown; of these, N_2 and W_2 were parallel cultures illuminated from nine in the morning to nine at night, while N_3 and W_3 were a second pair of parallel cultures illuminated from nine at night to nine in the morning.

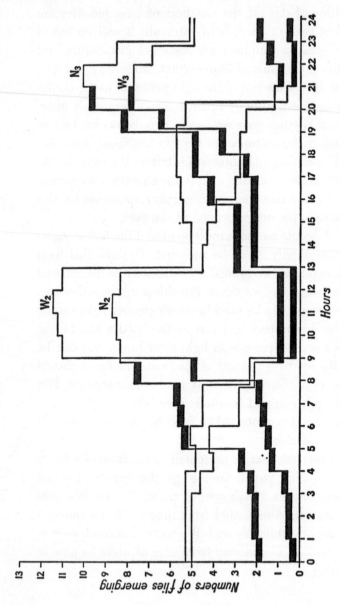

Fig. 31. Histogram indicating the number of *Drosophila* flies emerging at hourly intervals from four *Drosophila* cultures during a week. The shaded horizontals indicate the periods when the cultures were in the dark; the thin horizontals indicate hours of illumination.

EXPERIMENT 88. Time of Maximum Hatching of *Diapheromera* Nymphs (63)

Animals and apparatus: Several hundred stick insect eggs; petri dishes; light-tight cardboard box; dark room; table lamp; squared paper.

The eggs laid by a stick insect colony can easily be collected and separated from the dried bits of leaf and dead insects and feces. First sieve them through a colander and then pick them out from the feces and smaller detritus by hand. If one or two petri dishes are thickly sprinkled with eggs, observations can be made on the time of hatching. Particularly good results will be obtained if the dish is kept in a dark room under a table lamp—which should be left burning for a period of three or four hours, at the same time every day. But dark covers, made of cardboard can also be used. The periodicity can then be readily detected in a histogram drawn on squared paper (Fig. 32). The rhythm goes on in permanent darkness, but not if the eggs are exposed to continuous illumination. The twenty-four-hour rhythm can be temporarily lengthened by keeping the dish in darkness, and at a lower temperature after the eggs have been exposed to intermittent lighting. By transferring the dish to a higher temperature, in the dark, the rhythm can be temporarily quickened. Changes in temperature can be effected simply by enclosing the petri dish in a flat, light-tight cardboard box and by putting it closer to or farther from the electric bulb. For the convenience of the experimenter, the illumination should be at night, because most nymphs hatch during the dark period. In these circumstances, hatching will occur during the daytime, and no counts of hatched animals need be done during the night. Hourly or two-hourly counts can be made during the peak period.

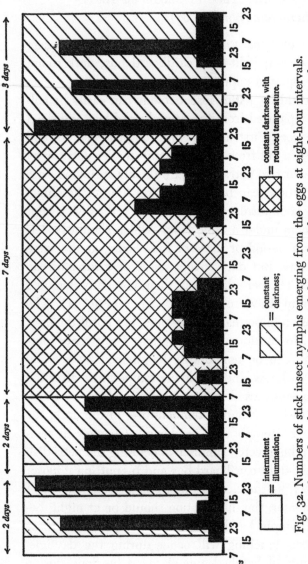

Fig. 32. Numbers of stick insect nymphs emerging from the eggs at eight-hour intervals. When subjected to the normal changes of day and night, most nymphs emerge after midnight, as shown in the first two days. If the eggs are then kept continuously in the dark, the peak period remains the same for the next two days. Keeping the eggs in the dark at a considerably lower temperature prolongs the emerging rhythm, so that only two peaks appear during the next week. The old peaks reappear, however, when the eggs are again kept in darkness, but at a normal temperature. White background represents illumination; crosshatching represents darkness.

In a different type of experiment it can be shown that a twenty-four-hour rhythm can be induced at high and low temperatures.

EXPERIMENT 89. Production of Eggs and Feces by Stick Insects during the Twenty-four Hours (63)

Animals and apparatus: Adult stick insects; glass funnel about 8 inches in diameter; glass cylinder; wire gauze; test tube; adapted alarm clock (if desired).

Most of the activities of the majority of insects show a diurnal periodicity. Some reach their maxima by day, and others by night, while still others show two or more maxima. Anybody who has watched a colony of stick insects (page 45) knows that they are more active during the night than during the day. In addition to finding this out by direct observation of their motor activity, it can also be inferred from the area of leaf which is consumed during the two periods and by more refined, so-called actographic methods (Experiment 18). The demonstration that both egg laying and the deposition of feces are mainly nocturnal is facilitated by the fact that eggs and feces are merely dropped by the insects. The only apparatus needed is a fairly large glass funnel and a glass cylinder. The funnel is fixed in a stand, and the cylinder, containing some leaves and about half a dozen adult stick insects, is stood in it resting on a piece of wire gauze. The stalk of the funnel hangs into a dry test tube. Counts should be made every three or four hours of the eggs and feces that drop into the test tube. Before each count, the funnel and cylinder should be gently shaken several times, so that any of the particles caught in the leaves or on the gauze are dislodged; and care must be taken to see that the funnel does not get blocked. The numbers collected over several days can be arranged in a histogram. A more mechanized form of the experiment can be performed by putting the funnel above a disk covered with flypaper, which is turned by the clockwork of an alarm clock (Fig. 33) (in the same way as in Experiment 18). If sectors are marked in advance, eggs

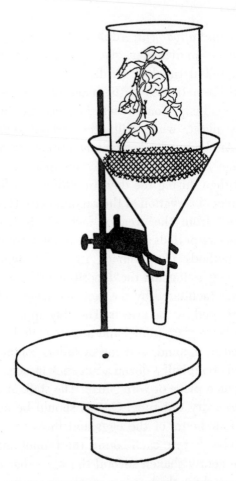

Fig. 33. Arrangement for recording the diurnal deposition of eggs and feces in the stick insect.

and feces can be counted in sectors corresponding to the time periods.

The experiment may then be repeated, keeping the whole arrangement in a dark room and recording the droppings under conditions of uniform darkness. It will be found that the diurnal rhythm will go on for some time.

EXPERIMENT 90. Time Sense in Bees (3, 57)

Animals and apparatus: Bees; marking equipment as in Experiment 101; petri dishes; syrup, 50 per cent sugar solution; milk bottle; filter paper; refrigerator.

Having tea regularly in one's garden can be very unpleasant when bees have found the jam and honey and crawl all over the place. If such a state of affairs arises, it can be noticed that very few bees will come to the spot all through the day; but when teatime approaches, clouds of bees may swarm around the place even before the tea is brought out. If the training method described in Experiment 84 is used, this apparent time sense in bees can be investigated in more detail.

Bees are fed on a petri dish filled with syrup for a period of two hours—say, between eleven and one o'clock—on three successive days. On the third day, some of the visitors are marked as is described in Experiment 101. At eight o'clock on the next day, an empty petri dish is presented. An observer counts the bees visiting it and notes down the numbers in half-hour intervals (it is worth while to begin to record the numbers from about half past nine onward). The visit of each marked bee is entered as a single event, and the visit of an unmarked one by a tick; the record can be kept until the afternoon, when no more bees will come. If a graph of the numbers is drawn as in Fig. 34, it will be found that the times at which the maximum number

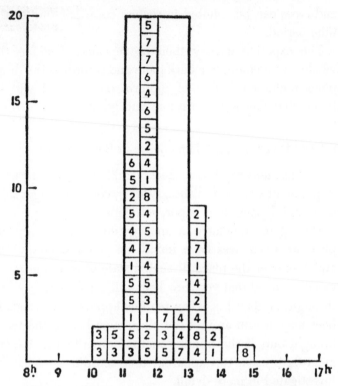

Fig. 34. Diagram showing the visits of marked bees trained to feed between 11 A.M. and 1 P.M., on a day when no honey is offered. The numbers in the squares indicate individual marked bees. The frame covering the squares indicates feeding time.

of visitors is recorded correspond to the regular feeding times. It is possible to train the same bees to come at two or even three different feeding hours, and even to accustom them to coming to a place *A* in the morning and to another place, *B*, in the afternoon. Curiously enough, it will be found that on the day when the counts are made and when no food is presented in either place, some bees—having found no food at the breakfast place—will try the tea place, and vice versa; so that two correct and two spurious visiting maxima occur. For this experiment two observers, of course, are needed.

It can be shown that the time sense of bees is dependent upon some internal periodicity in the insect's metabolism. This can be popularly expressed by saying that the bees are their own watches and are not entirely dependent for telling the time on environmental factors such as the sun. The speed of this internal mechanism can be increased or decreased by chemical and physical means. One may catch some of the marked bees at the end of the last feeding period, put them in a milk bottle containing some damp filter paper, and leave it in a refrigerator which is not quite freezing (6°–10°C.). If the bees are released after having been in the cold for several hours, some of them will visit their training place on the next day, later than their usual time by the length of their incarceration. Some individuals, however, may be influenced by the activities of untreated companions in the hive.

EXPERIMENT 91. Change in the Flight Direction of a Visiting Bee (64)

Animals and apparatus: Marked bees; feeding dish; forceps; filter paper; stop watch if possible.

There must be some factor that causes a bee to fly either away from the hive to collect pollen or nectar, or toward it on a homeward journey. There are two possibilities: One is that it is a physiological condition that determines the direction of flight; and the other is that it is the experience of having collected or having deposited the food that decides whether the bee shall fly inward or outward. The latter theory may hold good in the case of pollen gatherers; but in the nectar-collecting bee it can be shown that the filling of the honey bladder is a decisive factor in determining direction.

To demonstrate this, a marked bee is trained to a feeding dish and the times of its visits are observed—every time when it takes off from the dish and when it arrives again being noted. It may perhaps be found that that particular worker will spend about a minute in imbibing the solution and about two minutes in flying to and from the hive and in getting rid of the syrup. A fair degree of regularity is found, lasting sometimes for many hours. The next step in the investigation is to lift the bee by its wings with a pair of forceps and throw it into the air. If this is done a few seconds after the bee has begun to drink, it will usually return to the dish straightway and go on feeding. If, however, it is thrown into the air at the end of the feeding period, it will go home first and then return after about two minutes. The change in behavior occurs at about half-way through the feeding time. Thus, it is probably the amount of nectar that has been imbibed, and the consequent tension of the honey bladder which is perceived by the bee, that decides the direction of the flight.

It can be shown that the weight is not the decisive factor. For if a little ball of wax corresponding to the weight of the imbibed nectar (about 0.01 gms.) is stuck to the bee's abdomen, the bee will not return to the hive as long as the honey bladder is empty. Further, it can be shown that it is not the period of drinking which is decisive: if the posterior end of the abdomen of a sucking bee is clipped off with a pair of scissors, the bee will go on pumping syrup through its gut for many minutes—i.e., for much longer than the normal time—and will only stop when it succumbs to its wounds. Another way of changing the tension of the honey bladder is to make the bee disgorge its food as it does in the hive. This is fairly simply managed by seizing the bee by its wing with a pair of forceps, holding it standing with its legs on a table, and then gently pressing the abdomen with the finger. If this is done with a bee which has been feeding for about fifty seconds, it will readily disgorge one or two drops of nectar. Then if it is thrown into the air, it will usually return to the feeding place and refill the bladder, instead of taking off to the hive as it would otherwise have done. To avoid the bee's getting soiled with nectar, the drops should be taken off with filter paper.

An additional disproof of the suggestion that weight or memory is of primary importance in this connection is found in the fact that bees collecting on flowers do not as a rule get the whole of their supply from one source, but have to visit many flowers, often hundreds, during one excursion. It is thus most likely that a sensation comparable to our own feeling of a full or an empty stomach causes the difference in behavior between a homing or a foraging bee.

CHAPTER XI

Growth and Development

EXPERIMENT 92. The Growth of Stick Insects from One Molt to Another (20)

Animals and apparatus: Stick insects; balance; calipers or dividers; millimeter-squared paper.

Molting occurs in insects as it does in all the other arthropods. This means that at intervals they shed the cuticle under which a new, soft cuticle has been formed; and this latter then expands and hardens.

At the end of the last century, W. K. Brooks found that the larvae of the crab *Squilla* increased in length at each molt by about a quarter of their own length. Later on a similar law of growth was found in caterpillars, mantids, and various other insects. It was not clear why this regular increase should occur, and in fact many exceptions were found to the rule. But there are various species in which the linear measurements, for instance the length of the appendages, seem to obey it. A similar regularity may hold good, too, for other measurements. A possible explanation might be that most of the cells of the animal divide once between two molts, and each grows to the original size, thus doubling the volume. The cube root of 2 is approximately 1.26, and this roughly indicates an increase in linear dimension of one quarter. This description is too simple, however, as various tissues grow at different rates. The increase in size between molts of various insects differs somewhat; it is not always the same during consecutive nymphal stages.

The stick insect molts about once a month and increases in length at every molt until it reaches maturity after the sixth or seventh. It is interesting to weigh individual stick insects just after each molt and record the results on a chart. At the same time, the length of the body can be measured, and also the length of separate parts of the body. For instance, measurements can be made of the length of the second thoracic segment, or of the femur of one of the legs, taking care, however, that the leg does not come off in the process (see below). The length of the antennae will not be found to obey the rule. The insect can be weighed on a chemical balance, while the lengths are measured with a pair of calipers or dividers and some millimeter-squared paper. The measurements should be recorded to the nearest quarter of a millimeter.

EXPERIMENT 93. Autotomy of Legs in Stick Insects

Animals and apparatus: Stick insects; etherizer.

Stick insects can shed their legs; and they usually do so if one of the legs is injured, or even if it is firmly held. Some of the grasshoppers, too, have the same power. In the stick insect, the joint between trochanter and femur has become fixed and is not used in locomotion; at this point the leg is broken and shed by muscular action and very little blood is lost. Both larvae and adults are capable of autotomy, and an individual can shed more than one leg. But etherized insects are incapable of autotomy, which shows that it is an active process.

Regeneration starts from the stump of a larval leg and becomes apparent after molting; but the stump of an adult leg, as a rule, only heals and does not regenerate. Autotomy occurs in other groups of arthropods, such as the harvest-men, and in vertebrates, where the best-known case is that of the lizard's tail.

EXPERIMENT 94. Regeneration of Legs in Various Orders of Insects (6, 75, 87)

Animals and apparatus: Silver fish; *Diapheromera* nymphs; meal worms; larvae of water beetles; two needles ground to knife edges; lens or binocular microscope.

Regeneration of the shed legs in the stick insect has al-ready been mentioned in Experiments 19 and 93. As a rule, a limb is regenerated only after a molt, and a limb which is lost in a mature insect is usually not regenerated. How-ever, in the Apterygota, where growth and molting can go on after sexual maturity has been reached, regeneration of a leg can be observed even in the adult. Silver fish (*Lepisma*) or the very similar *Thermobia*—which lives in rather warmer localities, such as the floors of greenhouses —can be used for experiments on regeneration. Different types of behavior can be found in members of the same order, for instance among beetles. If a leg is removed from a young meal worm, it will be found regenerated in the grown-up larva, and later on a normal beetle will emerge from the pupa. But an amputation of a leg from the larvae of most water beetles will just heal, and no regeneration will occur in the larval period; nevertheless, a six-legged beetle will emerge from the pupa. Another interesting form of regeneration is the replacement of one form of appendage by another. For instance, in a *Diapheromera* nymph an antenna amputated near the base can some-times be observed to regenerate in the form of a front leg (Fig. 35). This shows that in pathological circumstances different organs can be produced from the same tissue. Other types of abnormalities may often be found, such as multiplications and incomplete regenerations.

Fig. 35. Regeneration of a leglike appendage in the place of the right antenna in *Diapheromera*. (After Cuenot)

EXPERIMENT 95. Preventing Aphids from Producing Winged Forms (23)

Animals and apparatus: Growing plants in pots; aphids; light and dark cloches; electric light.

Most of our aphids show a complicated change of phases which keep more or less to the following order: In the fall a fertilized, wingless female lays eggs on a plant, which winter over and hatch in the spring as wingless females. These go on propagating parthenogenetically all through the favorable season until the autumn, when winged females and males hatch out; these mate and usually change their host plant. Now, it is possible to suppress the occurrence of winged forms, or to produce them out of season, by various means according to the species. One way of suppressing wing formation is to increase the length of day during the autumn by additional artificial lighting. This has been achieved in such species as *Aphis rumicis* or *A. forbesi*. On the other hand, sexual winged females can be made to appear early in the year by cutting down the period of daylight in the early summer. In other species, such as some *Macrosiphum*, changes in temperature are more potent in influencing the phases; whereas others react to wilting food plants, or to a combination of factors. It is difficult to decide in any special case whether the effect of the light or of the temperature is exerted directly on the aphids, or whether it acts through the host plants. It should also be mentioned that, in experiments of this type, forms intermediate between wingless and winged occur which are rarely found in nature. Most aphid species are difficult to determine, and therefore care must be taken that the plants used are all infected by one species only. The easiest way to perform an experiment is to make use of aphid infections on some hardy pot plant, such as pelargoniums, chrysanthemums, or nasturtiums. A decrease in length of day can easily be effected by covering one of two plants with a darkened cloche, and the control plant with a clear one for the three hours before sunset every day. Winged forms should then appear after a week or so. An increase of the day period can be effected by means of the same cloches and an electric bulb switched on for three hours after sunset every day. In this case, the aphids on the plant under the transparent cloche will get the additional light. It need scarcely be mentioned that the plants must not be kept under the cloches except during the stated periods. Winged and wingless phases of the same aphid species look very different; the former not only have

wings and ocelli but also larger eyes than the wingless
forms and usually a much darker body color.

EXPERIMENT 96. Dependence of Egg Laying and Subsequent Development on Humidity in
Drosophila

Animals and apparatus: Drosophila culture; food
medium; charcoal; four petri dishes; four glass jars; yeast
paste.

Most insects do not care for their offspring. In some
cases, for instance in the social forms of bees and wasps,
the young are cared for; but in the great majority of insects,
the eggs are merely deposited in places which are suitable
for their development. Among the many conditions that
are necessary for the healthy development of the eggs and
larvae, such as temperature, protection, and food, moisture
is perhaps the most important. The odor of the locality can
also act as a strong inducement to the insect to deposit
its eggs.

The influence of both humidity and smell on egg laying
in *Drosophila* can easily be demonstrated. Four petri
dishes are filled almost to the brim with food, prepared in
the way described on page 171, but with the addition of a
teaspoonful of powdered charcoal mixed into the food to
make it black. When the food has set, one dish is left open
to the air for a day to dry up in a warm room, the second is
covered with its lid, and the third and fourth are thickly
painted with a yeast paste and covered. Four glass jars
are needed whose mouths are wide enough to cover the
petri dishes. Into each of these jars a dozen well-fed female
Drosophilae are released; after their lids have been removed, the jars are then inverted over the dishes containing the food. A day later the dishes are inspected. There

will be hardly any eggs on the dried-up dish, a few on the dish that was not painted with yeast, and many more on the two dishes that were painted. The eggs are visible to the naked eye; they are white and appear rather like little barrage balloons against the dark food medium.

The two yeast-painted dishes are subsequently treated differently. One is kept under the glass jar, but without any flies, while the other is exposed to the dry air of the room. The larvae which hatch out in two or three days will develop in the covered culture but not in the exposed one.

EXPERIMENT 97. Length of Pupal Development in *Tenebrio* (73)

Animals and apparatus: *Tenebrio* pupae; matchboxes; cotton wool; two thermometers, maximum and minimum if possible.

The duration of pupal development in many Lepidoptera and Coleoptera is shorter at high temperature and longer in the cold. The relationship between time and temperature is usually not straightforward, but it can easily be demonstrated within wide limits. For instance, if fresh pupae of the flour beetle are collected, it will be found that the length of pupation can be greatly shortened by keeping them at 30°C. instead of at 15°C. In making the comparison, it is usually sufficient to collect pupae daily in a culture of meal worms and to put them each day into a matchbox with some cotton wool, writing the date of pupation on the box. Half the matchboxes are then left in a warm place (whose temperature, however, should never exceed 32°C.), and the other half in a cool room (which should never be colder than 14°C.). The number of beetles which have emerged are then scored daily, and the times of development in the two groups are compared.

CHAPTER XII

Behavior

EXPERIMENT 98. Flower Constancy and
Small Area of Collecting in Honey Bees (18)

Animals and apparatus: Marked bees; petri dish with
syrup.

If a honeybee collecting nectar on a flower is marked in
the way described in Experiment 101, it can be followed
for some time. Usually there is not very much nectar about,
and the bee will have to visit many flowers before it can
return to the hive to empty its honey sac. It will be found
that any one bee is constant to one particular kind of flower,
while neglecting other sources of nectar, at least at a certain time of day, in the same neighborhood. For instance,
it will go on visiting the apple blossom on a tree and pay
no attention to the dandelions underneath it. At other
times, bees may visit only the dandelions and not go near
the apple blossom. This very striking habit is called flower
constancy, and its significance lies probably in an economy
of effort. If there is a heavy honey flow, or if a rich artificial
syrup is provided, a bee will confine its activity to a very
small area indeed, and even to one single flower or source
of food. It even shows a considerable regularity in its approach to the feeding place. For example, it may alight
always on the same bit of a petri dish, or first settle on a
grass leaf in the neighborhood, and so on. By marking a bee
at a particular place in the flowering field, and by observing the range of its searching activities, it is possible to

determine the area over which its activity ranges. It is usually only a few square yards. This has to be taken into consideration in the cultivation of plants in which pollination is an important matter and which depend upon bees to effect it.

CHAPTER XIII

Population

EXPERIMENT 99. Number and Size of Larvae in a Given Volume of Culture Medium

Animals and apparatus: Inseminated *Drosophila* females; tubes 1 inch by 5 inches; culture medium; filter paper; cotton wool; etherizer.

The amount of food available in a culture for each individual may determine its development. Thus, when only a certain amount of food is available, larger or smaller pupae and adults will develop according to whether there were few or many larvae present in the original culture. If the competition is very great, even death may result. On the other hand, many species are known in which the individuals, without being actually social, do thrive better in groups than when they are alone. This applies to *Drosophilae* living on a yeast-producing medium.

It is believed that an optimum productivity of the food medium is dependent on the burrowing of the larvae, which "plow up" the medium. This process mixes and aerates it, so that more yeast cells are produced; and these, in turn, are eaten by the larvae. To determine the optimum population in a culture, the following procedure may be adopted: Two dozen tubes, each 1 inch by 5 inches, are filled to a depth of about an inch with maize-agar-yeast medium (page 171) and are left to cool. A paste is then prepared from half an ounce of baker's yeast and two tablespoons of water, and the congealed surface of the medium is heavily painted with this mixture. A piece of filter paper 1 inch by 2 inches is thrust into the food layer in each tube, and all the tubes are stoppered and labeled with numbers from 1 to 24.

About 130 inseminated females (p. 172) are selected from an etherized batch of flies, and one is put into each of tubes 1–8, two into tubes 9–12, four into tubes 13–16, eight into tubes 17–20, and sixteen into tubes 21–24. Great care must be taken to make sure that none of the insects is drowned. The flies from tubes 1–4 are released after two hours, but those in tubes 5–24 are left indefinitely. The tubes should be kept at a temperature of about 25° C., and notes should be taken of the dates of emergence of flies and of their size and number.

EXPERIMENT 100. Counting Larvae of
Crane Flies ("Leatherjackets") in a Given Area

Apparatus: Orthodichlorobenzene; watering can; twelve rods one yard long; closely cut lawn near a fence or hedge.

The larvae of crane flies live in the roots of turf and of other plants, where they may cause considerable damage. Gardeners and greenkeepers are therefore interested in keeping down their numbers. Sampling soil insects is a very laborious task, but a method has been found of driving practically all the crane fly larvae in a given area to the surface.

To find out how many there are in the ground at any particular time and place, several samples are needed. If, for instance, a lawn is to be studied, three areas, each a yard square, should be marked out with yardsticks. Each of these areas should be watered with orthodichlorobenzene in solution. Two gallons of a 0.3 per cent solution are needed for one square yard. Half an hour after the treatment crane fly larvae, as well as some other soil insects and some earthworms, will have come to the surface and can be counted. The animals, however, are not killed; and if left alone they will return into the earth, provided that they are not picked up by birds in the interval.

The way in which orthodichlorobenzene acts is not quite clear. But presumably it causes an urge to crawl upward by making the respiration of the animals difficult. This probably also applies to the earthworms, which are known to come to the surface of the ground when the soil is waterlogged by rain.

CHAPTER XIV

Technique

EXPERIMENT 101. Marking Bees (42)

Animals and apparatus: Bees; paints as described; fine paintbrushes.

If the behavior of an individual worker bee is to be studied, it is essential that one should be able to recognize it. It is even more necessary to be able to distinguish between the different bees of a trained crew.

Various methods of marking can be used for this purpose. Some observers have made use of small paper disks with figures printed on them, which have been glued onto the bee's thorax; but the figures can be read only at a short distance, and the disk is easily lost. A better method consists in combining color and position in the following way: Five colors are used—red, yellow, green, blue, and white—and these can be applied in five positions on the bee's body. The thorax is regarded as being divided on its dorsal surface into four quadrants: red in the left frontal quadrant means 1; in the right frontal quadrant, 6; in the left caudal quadrant, 10; in the right caudal quadrant, 60; and on the abdomen, 100; yellow means 2, 7, 20, 70, or 200 according to position; and so on. By combining color and position in this way, it is possible to identify 599 bees, which is a larger number than is usually needed for experimental purposes.

Various types of paints can be used. For instance, either oil paints or paints mixed with shellac in alcoholic solution are suitable. But probably the best paint is prepared by dissolving sufficient resin in acetone to give a paint of good consistency, and then adding to this sufficient water-color (or oil) pigment from an artist's tube to give the intensity of color required. The paints should be set up in small vessels with lids, and a fine-pointed brush must be used for applying each color. The brushes should be washed in whatever solvent the paint is contained in.

It is not necessary to catch the bees, for they can be painted while they are sucking syrup from a dish, a process which lasts for about a minute.

Appendices
A. TECHNICAL NOTES

To Obtain Carbon Dioxide from a Soda-Water Siphon

Ordinarily soda-water siphons are used to produce water which is supersaturated with carbon dioxide. By holding a half-empty siphon upside down, gaseous carbon dioxide can be released from the spout; and if some rubber tubing is attached to the spout, a flow of carbon dioxide can be obtained for some time (Fig. 36). Mixtures of

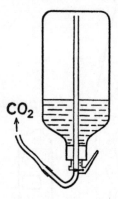

Fig. 36. Inverted soda-water siphon with attached rubber tubing, showing how small quantities of carbon dioxide can be obtained.

carbon dioxide and air can also be obtained by using one of the devices for recharging siphons at home, but without adding any liquid. In this case, the siphon need not be held upside down when the gas is being released.

Etherizer

Ether vapors cause a reversible immobilization in most insects. But contact of the cuticle with liquid ether, or even with water saturated with ether, is fatal to the majority of adult insects; and care must therefore be taken in using an etherizer to insure that it is perfectly dry before use. As most commercial ether contains some water, the liquid in the cotton wool in the hollow stopper tends to become rich in water after some time, as the ether evaporates more quickly than the water. The cotton wool must therefore be replaced from time to time, or the lid must be dried in a warm place. (Fig. 37, c.)

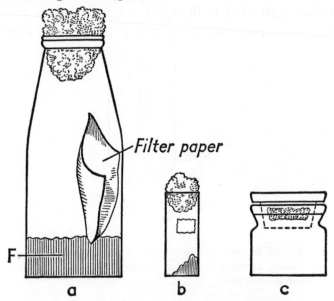

Filter paper

F

a   b   c

Fig. 37. (a) Milk bottle with a cotton-wool stopper containing food and a piece of filter paper. (b) Flat-bottomed tube with label, for smaller cultures. (c) Etherizer made from a wide-necked bottle with a hollow stopper; a piece of cotton wool is fixed into the hollow of the stopper and is moistened with ether.

APPENDICES 169

Killing Bottles

Carbon tetrachloride bottle. Carbon tetrachloride vapors in a sealed jar may be used to kill insects for one's collection. The jar should have a wide mouth and a screw-on lid. Pour into the bottom a half-inch layer of plaster of Paris mixed to the consistency of cake batter. When this hardens, the bottle is ready for use. Add several drops of carbon tetrachloride to the absorbent plaster. Cover this with a disk of cardboard to prevent direct contact of insects with the carbon tetrachloride. Do not put beetles and butterflies or moths in the bottle at the same time, lest damage be inflicted on the latter.

B. CULTURE METHODS

The Vinegar Fly (Fruit Fly, Banana Fly), *Drosophila melanogaster*

Various species of *Drosophilae* can be caught or trapped in the neighborhood of such places as orchards, vinegar factories, and fruit shops. Their larvae are found in fermenting fruit, in the bleeding sap of trees, and in many other kinds of decomposing organic matter. In the late summer, the flies are frequently found on windowpanes, where they can easily be trapped with a vial and a bit of paper. Traps can also be laid for them on a fine day in an orchard. A simple type of trap consists of a culture bottle partly filled with the medium described below, or with rotting apple or other fruit, and having a three-inch length of the inner tube of a bicycle tire fitted onto the neck of the bottle. The free end of this is pushed into the bottle so that a sort of funnel is formed by which flies can enter, though they find it difficult to escape again (Fig. 38).

Drosophilae can be bred in many different ways; but usually they are kept on fermenting substances, where the larvae feed on yeasts. If only a few flies are needed, it may be simplest to breed them on bananas, grapes, or plums, in a milk bottle closed with a stopper made of a ball of cotton wool. But this procedure has the drawback that the food is easily shaken out when the flies are being removed, and the whole thing may get very messy. One way

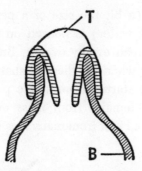

Fig. 38. Schematic drawing of a trap for catching *Drosophilae*, made from a food bottle (*B*) and two inches of the inner tube of a bicycle tire. The tubing is drawn over the neck of the bottle for half its length, and the other half is turned into the neck of the bottle.

of avoiding this is to use vials of about one inch in diameter and five inches high, with a piece of filter paper on top of the pulped banana, which should be about one inch deep (Fig. 37, *a*). The most satisfactory way of making cultures, however, is to use an artificial medium made as follows: 50 cc. of water is boiled with 11 cc. of molasses; meanwhile 15 gms. of maize meal is mixed with 25 cc. of cold water and poured into the boiling molasses solution. This mixture is cooked until it will set as a jelly, but not long enough to make it too thick to pour conveniently when it is still hot. Finally, a tablespoonful of rolled oats is added to the mixture. It is useful to stir in a pinch of an anti-mold preparation, such as nipagene or moldex, but this is not essential. The food must be poured into the bottles or vials to a depth of about one inch, and it is important to avoid spilling it on the top or sides of the container. In each bottle a strip of filter paper is put with its end in the food, so that the larvae can crawl onto it to pupate. After the medium is cool, a few drops of a suspension of baker's yeast in water (a bit the size of a pea, ground up in a tablespoonful of water) is poured on the surface of the medium and spread evenly over it. But no liquid should remain standing when the flies are shaken into the bottle. Cultures can be started from single pairs, single insemi-nated females (females from mass cultures more than thirty-six hours old), or from many flies (Fig. 39). The best

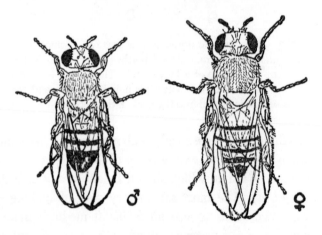

Fig. 39. Male and female *Drosophilae*. The flies are about 3 mm. long.

temperature at which to keep them is 25°C., but any temperature between 20° and 26°C. will do.

Stick Insects, *Diapheromera femorata*

Although several species of walking sticks are present in the United States, it is not always easy to locate individual insects. Their long, narrow, brown or green bodies allow them to blend perfectly with the twigs upon which they walk. The eggs, too, are difficult to recognize. In the fall, one hundred or more of the seedlike eggs are dropped by a single female. Finding these among the leaves, an amateur botanist is apt to plant them, fully expecting some new breed of greenery to sprout.

The most common stick insect in the United States is *Diapheromera femorata,* the eggs of which may be inexpensively purchased from several biological supply houses. Keep them in a petri dish in a warm room until they hatch, then transfer to a wooden-framed rearing cage covered with screen wire or muslin. Feed the nymphs on the fresh leaves from either oak, cherry, walnut, or locust trees. If leaves are unavailable, grass and white clover may be substituted. Sprinkle the leaves or grass occasionally with a few drops of water. Stick insects mature in about two months but may be used at an earlier date for some of the experiments described in this book.

Culture of the Flour Moth

Flour moths of the genus *Ephestia,* or related genera, are common pests in mills, warehouses, and bakeries. They live on flour, semolina, bran, rolled oats, and other cereals and can be kept on all these substances. But they do not do well on pure white flour owing to the lack of certain vitamins. A culture can be started from the females found fluttering about, or from some contaminated foodstuff, and is easily recognizable by the fact that the original material appears to be lumpy and matted together. The females and the foodstuff are put into a one-pound jam jar, filled to a depth of an inch with rolled oats, and loosely covered with cotton wool. The top is closed with muslin held in place with a rubber band. A good temperature for keeping the culture is about 25°C. The flour moth thrives best in a fairly moist atmosphere; therefore, the cotton wool should be moistened from time to time.

Ladybirds

Ladybirds are difficult to rear, and it is best to catch them whenever they are needed for experiments. This is easy at the right time of year, as they are very widely distributed and are often abundant on hedges and shrubs and in meadows and gardens. However, if it is desirable to breed them, it may be attempted by keeping them on plants infested with aphids in a glasshouse; pelargoniums, nasturtiums, roses, or any plants which are susceptible to attack can be used. Not only the beetles but also their larvae eat aphids.

Meal Worms, *Tenebrio molitor*

The larvae of the flour beetle are kept by many people because of their value as food for amphibia and reptiles. A culture is easily made in a large box—e.g., a large biscuit can—the bottom of which is covered with a mixture of flour and bits of dry bread to a depth of about an inch, underneath some old rag. Some meal worms are bought and put into the can, which should be loosely covered. Development will be quicker and better if the can is kept in a warm room and if the rag is moistened occasionally.

Blowflies and Houseflies

Some of the species of these flies can be reared comparatively easily; others are more difficult. Blowflies usually require meat or fish and a rather large wire cage; but the cultures are smelly and cannot be kept in inhabited rooms. The meat or fish should be in a dish, which is best placed in a box containing dry earth or sawdust. The grown-up larvae migrate into this substratum for pupation. Blowflies do well only at temperatures about 20°C. and in a moist, but not wet, atmosphere. It is often possible in summer to procure maggots and pupae from a faulty garbage can. In winter, they can be obtained from fishing-tackle shops. The grown-up maggots leave the container, so that one need not dig for them. Most species of houseflies are more difficult to breed, but the methods are less smelly. Some people find boxes of horse manure or earth satisfactory; others prefer hard-boiled eggs placed in flowerpots full of earth or sawdust, so that only the cut ends of the egg are exposed. A complete medium for rearing houseflies is commercially obtainable.

C. COMPARATIVE TEMPERATURES

Centigrade	Fahrenheit
20	68.0
25	77.0
28	82.4
30	86.0
34	93.2
37	98.6
40	104.0
45	113.0
50	122.0
60	140.0
70	158.0
80	176.0

D. ADDRESSES OF
BIOLOGICAL SUPPLY HOUSES
(and an abbreviated list of available materials)

The following list of biological supply houses will be useful in obtaining specific insects and equipment:

COMPANY NAME	LIST OF SUPPLIES
American Optical Instrument Division Buffalo 15, New York	Microscopes and accessories, eye charts, microtomes.
Bausch & Lomb Optical Co. 635 St. Paul Street Rochester, New York	Microscopes and accessories, projectors, ophthalmic instruments.
Burdick Drosophila Supply 614 Evergreen Street West Lafayette, Indiana	Large variety of *Drosophila* stocks, kits with fly food included, special ether anesthetizers.
Cambosco Scientific Co. 37 Antwerp Street Brighton 35, Massachusetts	Laboratory equipment, chemicals, preserved specimens.
General Biological Supply House, Inc. (Turtox)* 8200 South Hoyne Avenue Chicago 20, Illinois	Large supply of living and preserved specimens, laboratory equipment, microscopes and slides, skeletons, charts, models.
National Biological Laboratories P. O. Box 103 Falls Church, Virginia	Living and preserved specimens, slides, microscopes, skeletons and models.
Quivira Specialities Co. 4204 West Twenty-first Street Topeka, Kansas	Large selection of living and preserved specimens, slides, cages, foods, laboratory equipment.

* Prefers to sell only to teachers.

Research Scientific Supplies, Inc.   Microscopes and slides, pre-
Dept. 823   served specimens, fossils.
126 West Twenty-third Street
New York 11, New York

Ward's Natural Science Estab-   Living and preserved specimens,
    lishment, Inc.   microscopes and slides, skeletons,
3000 Ridge Road East   models, charts, animal cages,
Rochester 9, New York   laboratory equipment.

E. BIBLIOGRAPHY

REFERENCE   EXPERIMENT
NUMBER

1. Atzler, M. 1931. *Z. vergl. Physiol.* 13, 509–33   33
2. Baunacke, W. 1912. *Zool. Jahr. Anat.* 34, 179–346   59
3. Beling, I. 1929. *Z. vergl. Physiol.* 9, 259–338   90
4. Bethe, A. 1910. *Zool. Jahrb., Physiol.*   60
5. Bliss, C. I. 1935. *J. Econ. Ent.* 29, 37–54   10
6. Brecher, L. 1924. *Arch. Mikr. Anat. Ent. Mech.* 102,
   549–72   94
7. Brun, R. 1914. *Die Raumorientierung der Ameisen und
   das Orientierungsproblem im Allgemeinen* (Jena)   72
8. Buchner, P. 1930. *Tier und Pflanze in Symbiose* (Berlin) 3
9. Buddenbrock, W. von. 1917. *S. B. Heidleberg Akad. Wiss.
   Math. Nat.* 8B, 1–26   86
10. ——. 1921. *Biol. Zbl.* 41, 41–48   19
11. ——. 1931. *Z. vergl. Physiol.* 15, 597–612   74
12. ——. 1937. *Grundriss der vergleichenden Physiologie*
    (Berlin)   37, 41, 44, 57, 66,
                                            69, 73, 75, 79, 81
13. ——, and H. Friedrich. 1932. *Zool. Jb. Abt. allg. Zool.
    Physiol.* 51, 131–48   42
14. ——, and E. Schulz. 1933. *Zool. Jb. Abt. allg. Zool.
    Physiol.* 52, 513–36   74
15. Bull, L. 1904. *C. R. Acad. Sci.* 138, 590–92   21
16. ——. 1909. *C. R. Acad. Sci.* 149, 942–44   21
17. ——. 1910. *C. R. Acad. Sci.* 150, 129–31   21
18. Butler, C. G., E. P. Jeffree, and H. Kalmus. 1943. *J. Exp.
    Biol.* 20, 65–73   56, 98
19. Cappe de Baillon, P. 1936. *Bull. Biol. Fr. Belg.* 70, 1–35 65
20. D'Arcy Thompson, W. 1942. *Growth and Form* (Camb.
    Univ. Press)   92
21. David, W. A. L. 1945. *Nature.* 155, 204   25
22. ——, and P. Bracey. 1944. *Nature.* 153, 594   25

REFERENCE NUMBER		EXPERIMENT
23. Davidson, J. 1939. *Ann. Appl. Biol.* 16, 104–34		95
24. Dijkgraaf, S. 1947. *Experientia* 3, 34–50		47
25. Dolley, W. L., and Farris, E. J. 1929. *J. N. Y. Ent. Soc.* 37, 127–33		17
26. Dotterweich, H. 1928. *Zool. Jb. Abt. allg. Zool. Physiol.* 44, 399–425		23
27. Drosophila Information Service		5
28. Dürken, B. 1916. *Z. Wiss. Zool.* 116, 587–626		34
29. ———. 1923. *Arch. mikr. Anat.* 99, 222–389		34
30. Eastham, L. 1925. *Q. J. Micro. Sci.* 69, 385–98		9
31. Eggers, F. 1926. *Zool. Anz.* 68, 184–92		39
32. ———. 1927. *Zool. Anz.* 71, 136–56		39
33. Flügge, C. 1934. *Z. vergl. Physiol.* 20, 463–500		53
34. Ford, E. B. 1946. *Butterflies* (Collins)		35
35. Fraenkel, G. 1932. *Z. vergl. Physiol.* 16, 371–93		40
36. ———. 1932. *Z. vergl. Physiol.* 16, 394–460		15
37. ———. 1935. *Proc. Zoo. Soc. Lond.* 893–904	22, 30,	32
38. ———. 1940. *J. Exp. Biol.* 17, 18–29		8
39. ———, and D. L. Dunn. 1940. *The Orientation of Animals* (Oxford)		70
40. ———, and K. N. Rudall. 1940. *Proc. Roy. Soc. B.* 128, 1–35		32
41. Frings, H. 1945. *J. Exper. Zool.* 99, 115–40		36
42. Frisch, K. von, 1923. *Ueber die "Sprache" der Bienen* (Jena)		101
43. ———. 1926. *Bethes Handb. norm. path. Physiol.* 11, 203–39		58
44. ———. 1934. *Z. vergl. Physiol.* 21, 1–156		55
45. ———. 1946. *Österr. Zool. Zs,* I, 1–48		58
46. Gaffron, M. 1934. *Z. vergl. Physiol.* 20, 299–337		78
47. Götz, B. 1936. *Z. vergl. Physiol.* 23, 429–503		74
48. Gunn, D. L., and J. S. Kennedy. 1936. *J. Exp. Biol.* 13, 450–57		18
49. Harvey, N. 1940. *Living Light* (Princeton Univ. Press)		3
50. Hertz, M. 1934. *Z. vergl. Physiol.* 21, 463–67		51
51. Hundertmark, A. 1937. *Z. vergl. Physiol.* 24, 563–82		76
52. Hurst, H. 1941. *Nature,* 147, 388–89		26
53. Ilse, D. *Abstracts Zoo. Soc.* July 1, 1946		80
54. Janda, V. 1934. *Proc. Roy. Soc. of Prague. 2nd Ser.* 44		33
55. ———. 1937. *Proc. Roy. Soc. of Prague. 2nd Ser.* 46		33

REFERENCE   EXPERIMENT
NUMBER

56. Kalmus, H. 1929. *Z. vergl. Physiol.* 10, 445–55   24, 67
57. ——. 1934. *Z. vergl. Physiol.* 20, 405–19   90
58. ——. 1935. *Biol. Gen.* 11, 43–70   7
59. ——. 1935. *Biol. Gen.* 11, 94–114   87
60. ——. 1936. *Z. vergl. Physiol.* 23, 651–62   20
61. ——. 1937. *Z. vergl. Physiol.* 24, 644–55   76
62. ——. 1938. *Z. f. Tierpsych.* 2, 72–75   61
63. ——. 1938. *Z. vergl. Physiol.* 25, 494–508   88, 90
64. ——. 1938. *Z. vergl. Physiol.* 26, 79–85, 362–65   87, 91
65. ——. 1940. *Nature.* 145, 72   18, 87
66. ——. 1942. *Nature.* 150, 405   46
67. ——. 1942. *J. Genetics.* 44, 194–203   8
68. ——. 1942. *J. Exp. Biol.* 19, 238–54   10
69. ——. 1943. *Amer. Nat.* 77, 376–80   4
70. ——. 1944. *Nature.* 153, 714   28
71. Kennedy, J. S. 1939. *Proc. Zoo. Soc. Lond. Ser. A.* 109,
       221–42   77
72. Knoll, F. 1926. *Abhandl. Zool. Bot. Ges. Wien.* 12,
       1–616   82, 83
73. Krogh, A. 1914. *Z. allgemein. Physiol.* 16, 163–90   97
74. Loeb, J. 1915. *Science.* 41, 169   4
75. Megusar, F. 1907. *Arch. Ent. Mech.* 25, 148–234   94
76. Minnich, D. E. 1921. *J. Exp. Zool.* 33, 173–203   54
77. ——. 1922. *J. Exp. Zool.* 35, 57–82   54
78. ——. 1922. *J. Exp. Zool.* 36, 445–57   54
79. Nieschulz, O. 1934. *Z. angew. Ent.* 21, 224–38   63
80. Nutman, S. R. 1941. *Nature.* 148, 168–69   1
81. Plateau, F. 1884. *Mem. Acad. Roy. Belg.* 45, 1–219   15
82. Pryor, M. G. M. 1940. *Proc. Roy. Soc. B.* 128, 378–407   32
83. Regen, J. 1913. *Pflüg. Arch. ges. Physiol.* 155, 1–10   50
84. Russell, E. S. 1942. *Proc. Lin. Soc.* 154, 195–216   49
85. Schmalfuss, H., *et al.* 1937. *Z. vergl. Physiol.* 24, 493–508   29
86. Schmidt, P. 1913. *Biol. Zbl.* 33, 193–207   43
87. Sweetman, H. L. 1934. *Bull. Brooklyn Ent. Soc.* 29,
       158–61   94
88. Szymanski, J. S. 1914. *Pflüg. Arch. ges. Physiol.* 155,
       343–418   18
89. Thomsen, E., and M. Thomsen. 1937. *Z. vergl. Physiol.*
       24, 343–80   63, 64
90. Tischler, W. 1936. *Zool. Jb. Physiol.* 57, 157–202   76

REFERENCE   EXPERIMENT
NUMBER

91. Tonner, F. 1935. *Z. vergl. Physiol.* 22, 517–23   45
92. Uvarov, B. P. 1931. *Trans. Ent. Soc.* 79, 147   63
93. Weber, H. 1929. *Z. vergl. Physiol.* 9, 564–612   48, 62
94. Weis, J. 1930. *Z. vergl. Physiol.* 12, 206–48   54
95. Weyrauch, W. K. 1929. *Z. Morph. Oekol. Tiere.* 15,
       109–55   38
96. ——. 1929. *Z. vergl. Physiol.* 10, 655–87   38
97. Wigglesworth, V. B. 1944. *Nature.* 153, 493   26, 27, 28
98. ——. 1944. *J. Exp. Biol.* 21, 97–114   27
99. ——. 1943. *Proc. Roy. Soc. B.* 131, 313–39   13

INDEX OF INSECTS USED

INDEX

mosquito, feeding and, 33–34
stick insects, 141–45, 172–73
see also Cultures and culture
methods
Electricity, charging flies, 64–65
Ephemerids, *see* May flies
Ephestia (flour moth), 173
larvae, phototaxis in, 116
Epidermis, 68ff.
Equipment, 167–69, 177–78
Eristalis larvae, 40–42
Etherizers, 168
Excretion, 12
in stick insects, 143–45
Expansion of wings, 52–53
Eyes, insects', 12
painting of, 81, 84, 111–12
see also Vision

Falling:
reflex in stick insects, 78–79
tarsal inhibition and, 77
Fannia, 105, 131
Feces, production by stick insects, 143–45
Feeding, *see* Food
Female insects, 14
crickets, hearing in, 86–88
see also Eggs and egg laying
Field crickets, hearing in, 86–88
Firebrats (*Thermobia*), 153
Fireflies, light production, 18
Flies:
anemotaxis in, 83
calcium carbonate in Mal-
pighian tubes of larvae, 27–
28
catching, 84, 131
culture methods, 170–72,
174–75
and cyanide, 28–30
droplets on wings, 56–57
geotaxis in, 101–2
immobilization of, 23–24

optomotor reactions, 125–27
phototaxis in, 115–16
puparium formation, 65–68
tarsal inhibition, 76–77
wax on cuticle, removing or
abrading, 59–62
wingbeat, 50–52
see also Blowflies; *Drosophila;*
Houseflies; etc.
Flight:
carbon dioxide and, 54–55
light and, 112–13
and tarsal inhibition, 76–77
temperature and, 53–54
wingbeat, 50–52
see also Wings; specific insects
Floating of *Chaoborus* larvae,
42, 48–50
Flour beetles:
darkening of, 63–64
pupal development in, 157–
58
Flour moths:
culture of, 173
larvae, phototaxis in, 115–16
Flowers:
blue preference in flies, 131–
33
flower constancy in bees, 159–
60
Flying, *see* Flight
Food:
for *Drosophila*, 20–23, 25–27,
35–36
for mosquitoes, 33–35
see also Cultures and culture
methods; Sugar; etc.
Form, sense of, in bees, 136–37
Formic acid for ant routes, 96
Frisch, K. von, 97
Fruit flies, *see Drosophila*

Gases:
poisoning by, 29, 66